Midnight Pages

A MYSTICAL WORKBOOK *for* WRITERS, INSOMNIACS *and* NIGHT OWLS

created by DIANE RIIS

CREDITS
Book cover and interior design by Andrea Schmidt, *a-schmidt.com*
Copy editing by Ginger Hanson

DO YOU NEED A BOOK COACH, EDITOR, OR BOOK MARKETING EXPERT?
If you are seeking an experienced author's coach, editor, designer or marketer for your nonfiction book project, visit *earthandsoulpublishing.com*

ISBN: 979-8-9851310-0-0
First Edition
Printed worldwide through KDP

For more Midnight Pages, printable worksheets, and writing prompts, visit
WWW.THEMIDNIGHTPAGES.COM or **WWW.THEWRITEWITCH.COM.**
They might just keep you up at night!

FOR RICK

BECAUSE ALL THE NIGHTS WOULD BE IMPOSSIBLE WITHOUT YOU.

&

FOR SAM

BECAUSE LIKE THE NIGHT, YOU ARE FULL OF CREATIVITY, WONDER, MAGIC, AND POSSIBILITY. BE YOU.

At night, when the objective world has slunk back into its cavern and left dreamers to their own, there come inspirations and capabilities impossible at any less magical and quiet hour. No one knows whether or not he is a writer unless he has tried writing at night.

–H.P. Lovecraft

INTRODUCTION

I am an insomniac and a night owl. I imagine you were attracted to this book because you are one of these or maybe both. Whether you are up because you like it or because you can't help it, I have something to tell you:

You are up for a reason.

If you are a writer as well as one of these other things, you're in luck. Those extra hours give you an advantage over people who sleep for eight hours then try to cram their writing into a normal working day. This extra time you have is a divine gift. When the bout of insomnia breaks and you have to jam your writing into a short and ordinary day, you might even miss it.

> *What hath night to do with sleep?*
> –John Milton

If you can't imagine there's anything good about being up late, and you feel tired and cranky in the morning or downright sick when the wakeful nights start piling up, then your challenge is to see yourself as chosen. Because the night has singled you out to tell you something. Your insomnia may vanish once you listen.

> *Not I, nor anyone else can travel*
> *that road for you.*
>
> *You must travel it by yourself.*
>
> *Perhaps you have been on it*
> *since you were born, and did not know.*
>
> –Walt Whitman

If you revel in the night and love the darkness, you know it's more than just quiet time. You look forward to the household going to bed, to the stillness, the hours stretched out in front of you. *There'll be time for sleep later.* Now is time when dreams take form and you create, write, release, and practice magic. If you look up at the black sky and see a blank canvas ready for your words, you already know that night is an infinite field of potentiality.

Night is certainly more novel and less profane than day. –Henry David Thoreau

My goal is to help you fall in love with the night, with your writing, and maybe even with your sleeplessness. I want to take the problem out of being up at night and help you see it as a deep, rich, even holy experience that might not last forever. Find the magic in it. Make it mean something. Translate the night into stories, journals, books, travelogues, treatises, scripts, poems, or even prayers.

The people who will be drawn to this book march to the beat of their own drum. More than likely you are uber-creative, imaginative, empathic, intuitive, a little quirky, spiritual, and, above all, *flexible*. Because the night has moods, and it doesn't always go the way we want it to.

It's not a coincidence you found this workbook. Just like it wasn't a coincidence when one night, toward the end of writing it, as I wondered if it was a worthy project at all, I took a break for an evening and found myself looking for a movie. I wanted something sweet, nothing very taxing, maybe a cheesy old classic. It was halfway over before it dawned on me: *Sleepless in Seattle*. I'm sure the Universe was winking. So, now, you're holding it, my sleeplessness book for creatives and writers. You might as well read it with pen in hand and let the night wink at you too.

What is the night? –Macbeth

WRITING PROMPT

Imagine you are up because you're waiting on a call. Any minute the phone will ring. What news will the shadows, umbras, and night stars bring you?

To go in the dark with a light is
to know the light.
To know the dark, go dark. Go without sight,
and find that dark, too, blooms and sings and
is traveled by dark feet and dark wings.

–Wendell Berry

HOW TO USE THIS BOOK: WRITING PROMPTS

This book contains writing prompts, curiosities, inspiration, meditations, and provocations about the night. The prompts might seem a little different from ones you've seen before. They are creative exercises for pump-priming, pipe-clearing, insight-generating, and liberating your stuck, writerly self. But there's more.

HOW TO USE THIS BOOK:
MIDNIGHT PAGES

This workbook also introduces you to my invention, Midnight Pages. It's a writing practice for night people—for anyone who doesn't get up early enough to write "morning pages." We've all heard how productive we would be if only we got up an hour earlier than usual. *Just an hour would make such a difference!* For most insomniacs and night owls, that's just not going to fly. No disrespect to the creator and lovers of morning pages but if you're up all night,

5 a.m. isn't so magical. Maybe you've tried it. The house was quiet, an hour lay before you, full of potential. You wrote. It worked. *This might be the solution to not having time to write!* But soon you lost momentum. You remembered how you hate routine. It got harder to get out of bed when the alarm went off. And there was a price to pay for the early mornings. Because you don't like them.

Ugh, I'm only up at this horrible hour because it was the only appointment I could get.
–A true night owl about being awake at nine o'clock in the morning

Anyway, if you're a little contrary, a bit dark, "different," magical, weird, empathic, or nonlinear than most folks, midnight might suit you better.

Whether you come alive at night or insomnia keeps you awake with gritty eyeballs burning, this is what to do when you can't sleep: write.

MIDNIGHT PAGES ARE A REGULAR PRACTICE. You can do them every night at the stroke of twelve and make them true midnight pages. Light a candle, set a timer for thirty minutes or so, and free write until it goes off. Just write whatever comes, whether it makes any sense or not.

MIDNIGHT PAGES CAN BE PART OF YOUR BEDTIME RITUAL. Once the cold cream is slathered on your face and the hot water bottle tucked into the foot of your bed, climb in and write for thirty minutes. Finish with a question to take into your dream laboratory. Make no mistake, your subconscious mind is working all the time—especially in the dream time. Writing down your questions or requests puts your unconscious on the job. See what answers you get by morning. Leave the page open to record the dream that holds the solution to your dilemma.

OR MIDNIGHT PAGES CAN BE JUST FOR THOSE NIGHTS WHEN YOU CAN'T SLEEP. You won't get the same results as if you made it a nightly practice but then again, who am I to write off the strangely meaningful one-off exercise? Who am I to say one single, magical event can't change your life? Who says it's impossible that on a sleepless night, you start writing and get the insight of a lifetime? Maybe you will only need a single midnight page to change everything.

What are you going to do with the night?

ABOVE ALL, DO THIS:

Whether you are playing with the writing prompts or doing your Midnight Pages...

- Believe your inner writer. She has something to say.

- Stop stopping.

- Don't censor yourself.

- Write like the wind.

- Write long-hand if possible.

- Leave your inner critic outside.

- Don't distract yourself with food, drink, media, too much light, or even music. The inner gremlins want to take your mind, heart, and soul off writing and onto consuming, experiencing, and feeling. Don't let them.

A non-writing writer is a monster courting insanity. –Franz Kafka

MIDNIGHT PAGES

MIDNIGHT PAGES

I know many people who are devoted to "morning pages." My beloved book designer recently told me, "Oh, gosh, I did morning pages for years!" It's a writing practice from Julia Cameron's 1992 book, *The Artist's Way*. Since it required writing first thing in the morning, it never seemed a fit for a night owl like me. Sometimes I'm only just dozing off when other people are getting up early to dust off their morning pages notebook. I confess, I dismissed it without giving it a chance. I assumed there was "discipline" required—that was *implied* in rising early, wasn't it? You've got to be disciplined to get up before nine when you went to bed so late.

When sleep is erratic, a lot of things are changeable: moods, energy levels, and motivation being the top three. Early morning writing requires a constancy and regularity that insomniacs and night owls can't always pull off. Depending on how the night went, the best laid plans of any writer can go sideways.

These days, I understand the idea of discipline a little differently. Not to be confused with punishment (like getting up early), discipline is about devotion. It's about being a disciple of the thing we are devoted to: our writing. There is nothing to demand or force. There aren't any rules. We show up regularly to it because we love it. That's it.

Discipline sets the stage for magic.

Between every section or writing prompt in this book, you will find blank space for your Midnight Pages. You might need more paper; I am not trying to determine how long or how much you will write. Aim for thirty minutes, don't stop once you've started, and do not worry about how good, legible, or long it is. You can use Midnight Pages to:

- off-load the thoughts, judgements, ideas, and extraneous words that stick in your craw from the day and bog you down.

- help you keep writing without the pressure that it be "good" (or even make sense).

Notes

- prime the pump, spark your imagination, or focus your mind prior to writing.

- keep you tuned in to writing guides, higher inspiration, and your own inner wisdom.

- serve as a regular, head-clearing activity before you go to sleep.

- make use of the night for your own divine, creative purposes.

- enjoy the hours of the dark.

- write by the light of the moon.

- channel the spirits, guides, and guardians that have answered your call for guidance, help, insight, and relief.

GUIDELINES FOR MIDNIGHT PAGES

HAVE A VAGUE GOAL: Keep your goal simple and loose: time, word count, or page count. You can set a timer for twenty or thirty minutes and write until it goes off. You can decide on a word count and stop when you reach it (works great if you're typing rather than writing longhand). You could also use the two pages provided here as your goal. Having a stopping point is useful. Shooting for a minimal goal keeps us writing when the writing gets tough.

OTHERWISE, BE AIMLESS. Aside from your word or time count goal, have no purpose in mind. This isn't "aimless" as in "without value or meaning." This writing has real results: clarity, self-discovery, a smoother flow into more intentional writing, a way to tune in to our intuition. It primes the pump. It becomes easier to get started or to keep going. What we focus on grows, including a regular meditation or writing practice such as Midnight Pages.

WRITE FAST AND WITHOUT STOPPING: This is a practice of inspired free-writing. Oh, it's challenging not to re-read our work or want to go back and fix things. It's hard not to trail off and stare into space. You want to stop and think. To tap your pencil against your cheek-bone or twirl your hair. But this works only if you think less and write continuously. Write fast and don't take the pen off the page. If you're typing, keep your fingers moving. If necessary, repeat a sentence over and over. "I don't know what to write" works well. Notice I am not a stickler about writing longhand even though it has its advantages. I go back and forth between the keyboard and the notebook. See what works best for you.

HERE'S WHY THE NIGHT IS SO MAGICAL FOR THIS PARTICULAR WRITING PRACTICE: The night magnifies our imagination. Things go bump, and we're off, running wild, seeing things, watching shadows move, pulling the cord on memory, making connections we never made before. In these quiet hours you can imagine yourself to be the only soul awake at this time, doing this thing: creating when all the world is asleep.

WHAT TO WRITE WHEN YOU CAN'T THINK OF ANYTHING: If you get stuck and feel like you have nothing to left to say, keep repeating your last sentence. If nothing comes to you and that panicky, frustrated feeling comes up—the one where even the binding of the notebook irks you, remember, it's thirty minutes. When you know you're a fraud, even when you know these exercises are beneath you and an utter waste of time, remember, it's thirty minutes. You can do just about anything for that long. Keep going.

Instead of stopping and mentally searching for the next thing to write (which is using your brain and not the intuitive or inspired side of you), pick one of these sentences and write it over and over.

I am writing in the dark.
I am awake for a reason.
The dark has something to tell me.
What do you want to tell me?
What would be good for me to know?

You might be surprised what sentences creep in, answering your question or taking you off in an unexpected writing direction.

No one but Night, with tears on her dark face,
watches beside me in this windy place.
–Edna St. Vincent Millay

This is a workbook and not a book-book because I wanted there to be space for you to listen (to the night and to yourself) with your pen in hand. Even if you don't take up the practice of Midnight Pages, you can use the writing prompts and creative writing exercises and see what you come up with. You might devise a plot or sort out a vexation. When you have so many dark hours on your hands, anything is possible.

When I was putting this book together, I thought of my High Vibe Soul Deep Writing[1] students and how much paper they can go through in a night of writing with me. I know you'll need more blank pages than you'll find here, but it's a start. Soon, you'll get yourself a notebook to dedicate to it, and by then, writing Midnight Pages will be a habit.

So off we go! Write every night or on the nights you are up and cannot sleep rather than lie there on your bed becoming even more miserable. Turn on a (small) light or creep down the stairs, curl up on the couch, and see what the night has to say. Try the prompts, free write in your Midnight Pages, and, for goodness' sake, don't worry so much about sleep.

> *O seeker, Listen to your*
> *heart's true yearning.*
> *Don't sleep.* –Rumi

MIDNIGHT PAGES

MIDNIGHT PAGES

NYCTOPHILIA

Nyctophilia is a preference for the night or darkness. This is the world of nocturnal creatures like bats and vampires, the realm of imagination, dreams, and practicing magic. Witches conducted their spells and rituals under the cover of darkness; ancient worshippers of the Goddess held ceremonies under the dark or full moon. Nefarious plots are hatched; conspirators meet in the shadows. Danger lurks. Historically, night was filled with terrifying hazards, even if you stayed at home and didn't venture out.

Notes

For most (early modern) persons, the customary name for nightfall was "shutting in," a time to bar doors and bolt shutters once watchdogs had been loosed abroad. For night – its foul and fetid air, its preternatural darkness – spawned uncertain perils, both real and imaginary. –A. Roger Ekirch in At Day's Close: Night in Times Past

I bet you've been scared of the dark at least once, but you must also have ordinary and beautiful memories of the night—times when you preferred the night to the day. Remember summer camp when you were just ten? The nights were more magical than the busy, hiking, dusty days. You will never get the mildewy smell of the tent out of your nose, nor will you forget the ant-covered caramel apples nobody would touch.

Remember your first love and the date that went on past midnight when your beloved kissed you for the first time? Or maybe you recall the summery breeze coming off the lake at 1 a.m. after your high school graduation. Or you feel fondly for the first long nights of autumn once the clock has been set back and it falls completely dark by 5 p.m.?

What beloved nights have you?

I go to bed late. It's always been that way.
              –Sylvia Grace

WRITING PROMPT

Write about a night you loved or what you love about that night. Write a night scene for your character, or if you're writing your own life story, recall a night in times past.

Notes

Blame it on the movie Misery but when I lived in Kansas City, my favorite thing to do was a staycation in Lee's Summit. I'd book a room in the Comfort Inn off 291 and 50. There was a Perkins across the parking lot, and it was pre-COVID so continental breakfast and cable television. I took my laptop, printer, spare ink, lots of paper, legal pads and a new box of pens. All I did was write, edit, swim, eat and watch television. Oh, the Whistle Stop Café was on Main Street. Best damn coffee in the metro. I'd write all night, swim in the early morning...breakfast at the hotel, then drive to the Whistle Stop to edit and outline. I'd fall asleep watching TV early afternoon. Wake up, shower, grab dinner at Perkins, then repeat the whole process. God how I miss those days.
–Amy Buster, who says the magic hour for her is 4:00 a.m.

MIDNIGHT PAGES

MIDNIGHT PAGES

NOCTURNALIA

Technically, nocturnalia has to do with clothing, the regalia of a special evening—the way you'd dress for a party or event. But when I use the term, I don't mean the gown or tux or even the footie pajamas and fuzzy sweaters you wear to lounge around the house at 3 a.m.

T hink of nocturnalia as the way we are cloaked in the night itself, how it surrounds and covers you like blanket or cape. That covering changes your perception of the world and of yourself. As the dark wraps around you, the daylight-ordinary disappears. Perception shifts.

At night everything is more intense, more true.
–Elie Weisel

Nocturnalia can feel wonderful because it insulates you from the world's noise. It's a blessed relief—you can finally hear yourself think. Or maybe it's too quiet, and your first impulse is to distract yourself from the thoughts that come up. Probably the long history of associating monsters with the dark of night comes from this: now that you are listening to yourself think, the mental dragons and demons rise up

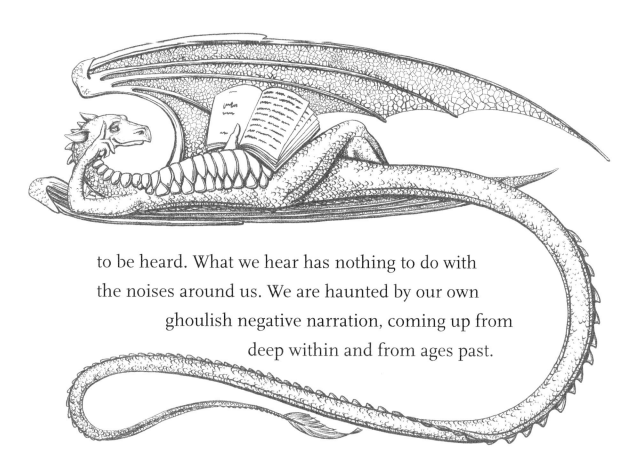

to be heard. What we hear has nothing to do with
the noises around us. We are haunted by our own
ghoulish negative narration, coming up from
deep within and from ages past.

The monsters and gremlins
you suppress all day fly free when you don't have to concentrate on work, focus on conversations, or handle long
to-do lists.

All these inhabitants of your subconscious have something
to tell you. Sit and listen then write their messages down.
I'd start with the dragons...

WRITING PROMPT

Sit and listen to the dragon who
hoards your treasure. Invite him
in—imagine him, write about him.
He has precious clues about how
you can lure him from the mouth of
the cave so you can claim the gems
and gold and magic that is yours.

MIDNIGHT PAGES

MIDNIGHT PAGES

NYCTOPHILE

The night is no man's friend.

–Old saying

A nyctophile is a lover of the night. Maybe you bask in the dark, loving how your sense of depth and distance changes. You watch the shadows lengthen, and as details grow indistinct, you feel a sense of relief and curiosity, maybe wonder. Even your familiar furniture looks strange as the dark enchants the room around you.

We are primarily visual beings. Many of us feel at a disadvantage in the night, handicapped by all that we cannot see. Though we think we "see" more clearly during the day, what we perceive is always filtered through our biases, expectations, and assumptions. Because we are receiving so many bits of data every second, our brain has no choice but to select and edit out the majority of what is happening within and around us in order to protect our delicate neurology. In any given moment, night or day, we are deleting more information and stimuli than we could possibly process.

The dark removes the input from our dominant sense: sight. Let the night show you what you normally cannot "see." Let your perception of reality widen out and trust what you notice. Who says night vision is any less real than broad daylight? *See me*, the night whispers.

WRITING PROMPT

Take an imaginative journey through a landscape of something you normally cannot see. For example, you might write about an animal that sees in the dark. You might step inside the interior of your body and tell a story about the workings of your brain or your digestion. Maybe you will write about meeting the inner gremlins who haunt your thoughts day and night.

MIDNIGHT PAGES

MIDNIGHT PAGES

MIDNIGHT PAGES

VIGILANTIA

Vigilantia: lying awake, sleepless, vigilance. The silence and stillness of midnight might feel suffocating, dense, and thick, heavy with foreboding. It might have you lying in bed, heart pounding, afraid of the dark.

Under the cloak of night, your non-visual senses are heightened. You hear things. They startle you awake when you drowse. The haunting memories, recriminations, and stuck thoughts keep you from your rest. Sometimes insights come up as well and sensations: the surge of adrenaline, pricklings on your neck. You might feel the weight of the dark bearing down on you, or you notice movement in the

Notes

shadows. Maybe you have the sense you're being watched. You feel there's something lurking in the dark that's imperceptible during the day. You might feel like you are not alone. Sometimes that subtle presence over your shoulder seems familiar. You wonder if it's been there before, maybe even always. During the day, with music blaring and people talking, you just don't perceive it. Ask what message all this has in store for you. Don't reject what you hear. Don't dismiss. Allow.

Night belongs to the spirits.
—Proverb

WRITING PROMPT

Close your eyes. What do you hear, smell, taste? What do you sense at an energetic or intuitive level? Spend some real time. Find at least twenty-five things. When it gets hard to add to the list is when it gets interesting...

1.
2.
3.
4.
5.
6.
7.
8.
9.
10.
11.
12.
13.
14.
15.
16.
17.
18.
19.
20.
21.
22.
23.
24.
25.

MIDNIGHT PAGES

MIDNIGHT PAGES

MIDNIGHT PAGES

DON'T SLEEP

The saints find their
treasure when the world is asleep;
for the sake of ever-giving love,
Don't sleep.
—Rumi

Rumi was the first person I'd ever read who told me not to sleep. Everyone else delivers lectures about how bad my insomnia is for me. How eight hours (all in a row) is ideal. It isn't healthy to string all-nighters together in order to finish my book.

If I fall for it, if I start to believe I should be sleeping instead of burning the midnight oil, I use a trick that works like magic. I lay down and tell myself I am going to stay awake to think through the next chapter of my book. Off to dreamland I go. But that is not where I want to be. I have the trick if I need it. But I don't plan to use it.

The breeze at dawn has secrets to tell you.
Don't go back to sleep.
You must ask for what you really want.
Don't go back to sleep.
—Rumi

WRITING PROMPT

The night is your magic carpet, the broomstick you ride through the clouds. It is the surfboard through the waves, the Lear jet flying you in luxury to wherever you want to go. Where is that? Tell me all about it—and don't neglect the feeling of the flight itself. Are magic carpet rides bumpy? I really want to know... (you can even post it on the Midnight Pages Facebook Group.)

MIDNIGHT PAGES

 # MIDNIGHT PAGES

MIDNIGHT PAGES

WATCHER, TELL US OF THE NIGHT

D id cave-dwellers, hunter-gatherers, horticulturalists,[8] and pastoralists of ancient times feel their hearts sink when they watched dusk descend? Did they worry that they'd never see the sun, the trees, the sky, or the faces of their loved ones again? Did they fear that the daylight would never return? Did they think that someday the Goddess would just forget to wake them up, and they'd stay in the dark forever? How did our ancient forebears sleep in a night so profound?

Maybe they couldn't see in the dark any better than we can but other senses compensated. The night was thick with thrashing, rustling, and growling. Real sounds and imagined ones carried far on the night air. Assuming ancient people had a heightened sense of smell compared to us, they knew their sweat and fear were pungent and fragrant to predators outside the cave. I can imagine myself inching away from a stinky brother or sister, hoping to keep my distance from this obvious, smelly target of the hungry sabertooth.

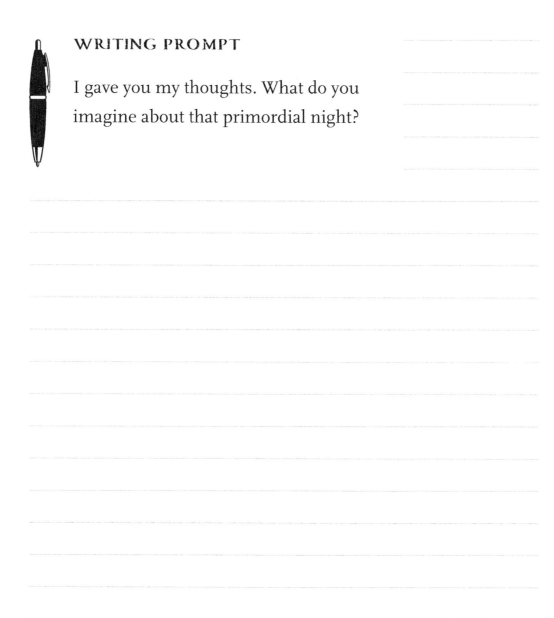

WRITING PROMPT

I gave you my thoughts. What do you imagine about that primordial night?

MIDNIGHT PAGES

MIDNIGHT PAGES

MIDNIGHT PAGES

SLEEP VIKINGS

Maybe the ancients got through their terrifying nights by allowing slumber to knock them out and carry them away. When my beloved falls suddenly off to sleep, he says he was "carried away by the sleep Vikings." I suspect it's actually the talking heads on the news channel that knocked him out. Or it was some inner wisdom that shut him down so he couldn't hear the doom and gloom of the news, so he'd be shielded from all the commercials for drugs and diseases.

Maybe our ancestors fell asleep like that, suddenly and completely, praying for dawn and desperate to avoid the perils that stalked them all around.

Having perfected the ability to fall asleep at will (and fast!) during turbulence on a plane or during storms (and high seas) on ferry boats, I can attest to how fast sleep can come and what a great knack it is to have: to be able to go unconscious when you're scared sh-tless.

WRITING PROMPT

If you're a fiction writer: Write a scary scene. Maybe you'll never use it, but put your characters through their paces anyway. Make them afraid. Very afraid. See how they evolve when you do it. See what they're made of. You've created them, but they have their own imperatives now. Give their fears voice.

If you're not a fiction writer: Write about a time when you were scared and why. What did you do; who came to your rescue? Did that day scar you forever, or did you find a way to cope with and resolve your fear? Tell me more...

Or try this: (You can post this one on the Midnight Pages Facebook Group. My son always wants scary stories to tell around the firepit!) Write a short horror story—you

WRITING PROMPT CONT.

know, the kind you heard at camp or at a sleepover. Write me the sort of story that is short and memorable enough for a kid to tell. One that gives kids goosebumps and an excuse to wake up a parent for an unnecessary Band-Aid.

MIDNIGHT PAGES

MIDNIGHT PAGES

E VIGLIO

Watcher, tell us of the night,
for the morning seems to dawn.
Traveler, shadows take their flight,
doubt and terror are withdrawn.
–Advent Hymn: Watchman
(Watcher) Tell Us of the Night,
John Bowring, 1825
Tune: Aberystwyth

Eviglio is to be on watch through the night, to be fully awake and alert. In 1966, Frederick Snyder proposed that "sentinel behavior" on the part of some members of the tribe allowed for our prehistoric ancestors to get a good night's rest.[2]

More recently, David Samson, PhD, a sleep researcher at Duke University, studied the Hanza tribe of Tanzania, a hunter-gatherer community, and determined that when people sleep together, several always remain awake, allowing the others to sleep. Samson and his collaborators say the sentinels are young, teenagers with better night vision, strength, and endurance than their elders. They suggest that this might explain (in part) why teens tend to stay up late. It is a hold-over from generations of young men (probably) who stayed awake, vigilant, so the rest of the family or tribe could relax.[3]

If you are an insomniac, does it stem from your role as a sentinel in another incarnation? Or maybe it's just a sign that the genetic wiring of the sentinel has been passed down to you. If you've ever asked, "Why am

I up?" in utter frustration at three o'clock in the morning, you can take comfort in this thought: throughout history, some members of the tribe have always stayed awake for the good of the whole, taking turns so everyone can get at least some amount of rest. That makes your insomnia evidence of your bloodline's heroism and sacrifice!

There are truths which one can see only when it's dark. –Isaac Bashevis Singer

There might be other reasons for your vigilance, of course. Maybe you wake up every night on the anniversary of the moment of your birth. Or maybe three o'clock is foretelling the hour of the night of your death. Maybe you're awake because there is something you need to know. What does your insomnia want to tell you?

WRITING PROMPT

Aside from indigestion, too much caffeine and sugar, aches and pains, why are you awake? I know you don't know the answer, but what if you did?

MIDNIGHT PAGES

MIDNIGHT PAGES

IMBOLC

Imbolc is also known as Candlemas, a Christianized pagan celebration of the return of Spring after a long winter's night.

Imbolc falls on February 2, Groundhog Day, and the Catholic church blesses candles in order to make a point: God has dominion over the forces of the "invisible world."[4] God is the keeper of light. He's in control. But the invisible world cannot be dominated or subdued. It is a part of the All, the Whole, the Divine and not separate from it. What did the church believe was contained in this invisible world? What was so terrifying? All things fae, witchy, feminine, unknowable, and uncontrollable, obviously.

Darkness is the bed of creativity.

Imbolc is from the Celtic Wiccan tradition, and it celebrates the wisdom of the earth. On this day, seeds begin to stir in the ground, responding to the changing light. Spring is coming. Imbolc is a party because the community survived the winter, and the seeds of future harvests begin their gestation in the womb of the earth.

All the buried seeds crack open in the dark, the instant they surrender to a process they can't see. –Mark Nepo

WRITING PROMPT

Think of the thick, deep silence of the night as a womb, a place of gestation and creative development. New things are born in the dark. They come squiggling out of the deep soil and wailing out of the womb. The night is an incubator. What wants to be born in you, from you, for you?

MIDNIGHT PAGES

MIDNIGHT PAGES

MIDNIGHT PAGES

MYSTIC DARKNESS

Now you're up and asking, writing and opening yourself up to the idea that maybe the night has something to tell you. What do you need to know? Do you hope to find a hidden secret from an unknown source? Do you long for a visitation from a departed loved one or a word of encouragement from an ancestor, guide, or angel? Do you need to hear—loud and clear—about a new direction for your life? Or get proof that your life isn't random and meaningless? Are you open to receiving a memo from the deep, holy, inner Divine Herself?

Your wakefulness becomes a spiritual urgency.

Try automatic writing for any of these answers and requests. Automatic writing, also called direct writing or inspired writing among other things, allows for a wisdom beyond your own. It bypasses the ego that struggles with words and worries endlessly about commas and "doing it right." It's not about that...

With automatic writing, whether you see it as a sort of channeling or just as a free-flowing writing-without-rules you should feel like there is no effort on your part. You are allowing the Muse, or the Spirit, (or a particular spirit) to write through you. Here's how:

- Sit quietly and allow your mind to fill with all the thoughts you have, whether they are positive or negative; whether they are related to your book or not. Let the busy brain be busy. Breathe and watch the thoughts.

- Once you have watched that melee for a while you will get bored of it, or start to get wound up and feel all sorts of things: unworthiness, curiosity, maybe even anxiety. You might feel frustrated but don't quit now! Sit and breathe some more.

- If you have specific questions or concerns, you can think about them too.

- Next, imagine all the thoughts becoming as small as grains of sand. Watch them shrink until you can't see or hear them. They are just flecks, dots, tiny bits of silt.

- Allow the sand to filter down through your body into your wise belly. Allow your unconscious or your intuition to sift them until only one or two messages remain. You will feel your brain empty as your thoughts grow fewer and farther between.

- From the couple of thoughts remaining, state an intention: "I now allow inspired or guided writing to come through me onto the page. Only that which is for my highest good is welcome. I am safe, protected and open to loving guidance."

- Place your fingers on the keyboard, or pen on the paper and wait. Allow time, breath, and space. Remember there is no ideal outcome. You might not receive anything relevant to your life or your writing project. You might find that words come easily, flowing through you as if from another source, but sometimes they won't come at all. It might take a while. Don't give up! Return the next night and try again.

- When you are finished, say thank you. You can give thanks for the divine guidance you received or you can express gratitude to your own heart and mind, which quieted enough to send you a message, even if it wasn't crystal clear. If there is nothing on the page at all, be thankful for the time, the breath, the paper and laptop. Gratitude is a way to soften the edges of just about everything in life.

Notes

Millions of people channel energy, entities, divine inspiration, departed loved ones, and benevolent spirits every night through their pens and typewriters. If that feels freaky to you, okay. Imagine automatic writing as inspired free writing. Let go of the judgements you have about your own work and allow words to flow. But, keep in mind, if you've ever read over your work in the light of day and realize you don't remember half of it, maybe you weren't the only one writing it.

If you want guidance from beyond yourself, the darkness is conducive, and all you need is intention, a little prayer or spell for protection, and the willingness to let your ego step to the side during your writing sessions.

The first time I led this exercise at a High Vibe, Soul Deep writing retreat, I got a question about whether some negative force or evil entity might "come through" when we do automatic writing. At the time, the question put a fear in me that I was leading a group into dangerous territory. I didn't worry about that when I was doing it by myself. The thought hadn't ever even occurred to me. But now I was responsible for others. And who knew what their psyches were brewing and inviting? Now I know the dangers we face come from the ego, the inner gremlins that won't shut up. We can be our own worst enemies, especially when it comes to creativity. As long as your intention is in the best interest of all, you are fine. This is a benevolent universe and most of what we find terrifying is human-made.

Notes

Here's a protective spell in case you want it. You can include it in your ritual (above) for automatic writing just before you begin watching your thoughts.

Begin by imagining yourself surrounded by a golden bubble of light. Within it, you are protected. Nothing can harm you. Feel it glowing. You can let it expand to enclose your room, your house, your loved ones, your neighborhood, or beyond. Next, simply say,

"Safe and protected I will be.
Guides and guardians come to me.
Spirits of love and good and light,
write me a message in the night."

And now, two pages to play with automatic writing. Don't worry too much about where it's coming from. Your deepest wisdom and higher self are also holy and often as inaccessible as the highest angel. Also, don't worry if it takes a while. Keep coming back to the empty page and allow. See what happens after a few nights.

> *Whatever satisfies the soul is truth,*
> *Do anything but let it produce joy.*
> –Walt Whitman

WRITING PROMPT

If you're not into automatic writing, here are some questions to clarify your questions, and maybe by clearing your mind, you'll find your own solutions.

What Divine guidance would help you make sense of your daily grind? What would you want advice about? What might the ancestor, departed loved one, or thousand-year-old spirit guide say? If you are an atheist, imagine you are consulting your inner wisdom instead of a deity. Imagine you are addressing the field of all potentiality, where everything energetic and material arises. What support would you like to see show up to help you with the struggles you are facing right now?

WRITING PROMPT CONT.

MIDNIGHT PAGES

MIDNIGHT PAGES

MIDNIGHT PAGES

METANOIA

Listening to the night could also give you results that are powerfully ordinary: for example, you might get unstuck from a plot point or have insight into why you feel blocked.

Notes

My theory is that once we surrender to the night—especially if we feel like we can't sleep, that something is waking us up and calling us out of our sleep—once we turn off the TV, the phone, and the busy thoughts, whatever was murky begins to make sense. Metanoia is about a deep and permanent shift in how we see things. Ordinary insights create profound shifts. Point yourself in that direction during your nightly vigils.

The nearer the dawn
The darker the night.
–William Wadsworth Longfellow

WRITING PROMPT

If tonight brought you a fundamental shift—metanoia—what would be different in the morning? Tomorrow, post-metanoia, you wake up and look out your window to see a sign. It says,

MIDNIGHT PAGES

MIDNIGHT PAGES

MIDNIGHT PAGES

COSMIC UNCONSCIOUS

The night is a carrier of portends and signs. Open up to it and the night will reveal its secrets and then you will be blessed with an unimagined sea of archetypes, images, and magic from the Cosmic Unconscious. That's good news for a writer or a creative. Words, lyrics, scenes, visions, plots, characters with full blown personalities will roll in waves toward you. Not only will your stories become richer, they will resonate within your readers' hearts because these symbols are universal, cross-cultural, and timeless.

> *I often think that the night is alive and more richly colored than the day.*
> –Vincent Van Gogh

WRITING PROMPT

List images, memories, songs, colors, ideas that are on repeat for you right now. Do you wonder why they keep coming back? Where do they apply in the creative work you are doing? How do your characters react to them? What does it feel like to paint these colors and sing these songs?

MIDNIGHT PAGES

MIDNIGHT PAGES

SOMNOPHOBIA

Somnophobia is the fear of sleep. That seems uncommon. In my search for night lovers, I found so much more information about people who are afraid to be awake! When I was researching this book for creatives and writers, I had in mind people who do things differently because they've always *felt* a little different. I expected that when I went looking, I'd find throngs of contented night writers and other creatives who enjoyed the pregnant darkness. Who embraced the *different-ness* of the night but I wasn't finding any.

Instead, I found groups, posts, sites, and links by and for truly unhappy, sleepless people. Not many folks seem to be having fun with wakefulness. All I found was evidence and support for the idea that staying up is bad for you. You need your sleep! You'll be demented by the time you're old—not sleeping kills brain cells! You'll gain weight, be depressed, a hazard when driving, unproductive at work and generally miserable. There were people genuinely suffering from exhaustion, but worst of all—most heartbreaking of all—was reading about how desperately worried people were about not sleeping,

"Oh, my doctor said I better get to sleep. At my age, I can't be up at night! He says it puts me at risk for Alzheimers! I have to get this fixed!" The speaker was a person in her mid-seventies with lifelong insomnia. Her hand was at her throat; there was panic in her voice and probably a prescription for sleeping pills in her medicine chest. Do you think she felt better after this conversation with her physician? Was she any better able to sleep?

I've been one acquainted with the night.
—Robert Frost

My search proved the news that being awake in the dark was bad. There was only one ideal way to sleep: straight through for eight to nine hours. Bypass the nighttime experience altogether. If you're not doing that, there's something wrong with you. Normal, healthy people sleep, right? So you took all the warnings: If I don't sleep I'm more likely to be obese and have high blood pressure.

You tried the sleep hygiene advice, and the harder you *tried*, the less sleep you got. The more the stress of not sleeping kept you awake at night. The more meds you needed. The more tips, herbs, websites, wine, groups about insomnia you used. But maybe we're not supposed to be mono-sleeping for eight straight hours. (By mono-sleeping I mean one block of unbroken time; a single sleep.)

Night is the perfect time to bask in misery, pound your chest, and woe is me. Go for it.

Before the appearance of artificial lighting, our pre-industrialized forebears enjoyed segmented sleep, what they called "first" and "second" sleep, not one continuous, uninterrupted binge. Biphasic or segmented sleep meant people would sleep for a few hours, wake up in the middle of the night, and instead of being agitated, tossing and turning, they got up. Instead of just lying there waiting to fall back to sleep, they got out of bed, sipped tea, read, chatted with the neighbors. They prayed or contemplated their lives. If their spouse was up, maybe they made love. It was a time when spouses could talk, and individuals had time to reflect on life. Eventually, they'd fall back to sleep until it was time to get up. In his book, *At Day's Close: A Night in Times Past*, A. Roger Ekirch finds hundreds of references to first and second sleep going back to the time of Homer.[5]

When I first heard of biphasic sleep patterns, I felt liberated. I thought I was sleeping all wrong. Four or five broken hours at night and an hour in the afternoon. What the history of sleep shows is that biphasic sleep can look like late nights and siestas, especially in southern latitudes. It can be a first and second sleep pattern that varies somewhat with the seasons and our circadian rhythms. There are even multiphasic styles of sleep, designed with the user in mind!

Three o'clock in the morning has become a trope for marketers, politicians, entrepreneurs, copywriters, and nonfiction authors too. Anybody who wants to sell something needs to know what "jolts their prospect awake at 3 a.m." The savvy advertiser who can frame their product or service as the solution can make big money. But what if waking up is perfectly normal, and there's nothing to solve after all? What if the idea of eight unbroken hours of sleep (mono-sleep) is an abnormal expectation, and there's nothing wrong with those of us who don't get it? We wake up in the middle of the night. Why panic? If it didn't worry us so much, what would we do with the time?

The last refuge of the insomniac is a sense of superiority to the sleeping world.
–Leonard Cohen

If we were less stressed about the length and the quality of our sleep, the sleep deficits we are accruing, and the fears about what all this sleeplessness means for our health and our future, we'd probably sleep better in whatever pattern was natural for us. Maybe we'd do what our forebears did. Get up, occupy the time in pleasant ways, and then when we felt sleepy again, roll over and doze off until morning. We all know that staring at the clock, waiting to go back to sleep, and dreading how we'll feel in the morning doesn't help at all.[6]

I expand my consciousness outside the walls and I listen to the night. The daylight hides the universe from us. In the night there's nothing in the way. I can't get there in the day. –Sue B.

WRITING PROMPT

How do you spend the
currency of your night?

MIDNIGHT PAGES

MIDNIGHT PAGES

INCONNIVUS

Inconnivus is an adjective meaning unsleeping or wakeful. It's another way to say vigil, that watchful, waking state that seems to come so naturally to some of us.

Among the shocking amount of research about how our forefathers and mothers slept, you will find something called the preservation theory. It says that "while humans evolved, hiding out overnight increased the ability to survive."[7]

Doesn't it make sense that laying low, staying still, and burning fewer calories would give us a better chance to evolve? So does staying out of sight of wandering panthers. But I'm more interested in psychological survival—getting through the fear—more than surviving an actual flesh and blood attack by a nocturnal predator. What made it possible to close our eyes at all considering how fangless and defenseless we have always been?

Defenseless under the night
Our world in stupor lies... –W.H. Auden

I believe that sleeping all through the night must've come later in our evolution because it was dangerous, unnatural, and ridiculous to think we could close our eyes for eight hours during the most precarious times and expect to survive to see daybreak. Maybe insomnia isn't about sentinel behavior (the idea that some of us stayed awake all night to protect the tribe) but comes out of ancestral memory of a time when it just wasn't safe to close our eyes for fear of very real predators and very potent imaginary ones.

May we be without fear by night and by day.
  –Atharva Veda XIX

Recent studies show that our prehistoric ancestors probably got about the same amount of sleep we do, based on research with modern-day hunter-gatherers and horticulturalists.[8] So much for the theory we need eight or nine hours per night. The averages are closer to six and a half hours. So it's a myth that we get less sleep than our forebears. Maybe that puts into perspective some of the warnings that poor sleep leads to dementia as we age, among other dire predictions of the future.

You're up. It's okay. Better to be in the now, even if that means you're awake in the wee hours. What does the night want to tell you tonight? Maybe more importantly, what do you want to tell it?

WRITING PROMPT

Dear Darkness (write to your
inner or outer darkness...)

Dear Inner Wisdom
who sees in the dark...

MIDNIGHT PAGES

MIDNIGHT PAGES

MIDNIGHT PAGES

MIDNIGHT PAGES

INSOMNIA

Before I stopped making it a problem, I struggled with insomnia. As a little kid, I'd count the four corners of my bedroom ceiling dozens of times each night, and I'd practice what I now know is mindfulness meditation. I remember the night I realized that I was thinking about thinking. And that awareness was a thought too. I had found the Witness behind my thinking mind. Insomnia gave me that gift of mindful awareness. Maybe it's what set me off on my lifelong, spiritual journey. I was too young to call it "insomnia," so I stayed in bed like I was told to and counted the corners for hours every night. For all I knew, that's what everybody did.

As a teenager, I spent the nights reading Stephen King (I still can't sleep with my back to a window because of *'Salem's Lot*), Betty Friedan, The Tibetan Book of the Dead, and Everything You Wanted to Know About Sex But Were Afraid to Ask. When my father called me in the morning, I'd slink downstairs, feeling lazy and guilty for not jumping up in time for breakfast. It was only the fear of his wrath that made me careful always to be in time for the bus.

I don't have to worry about missing buses anymore. I sleep little, go to bed late, wake up early, and shut down at precisely two o'clock most afternoons. It took years not to feel lazy about that. But that's me doing me—normal, natural, and perfectly okay—clocking in around five and one-half hours per night and one hour some afternoons.

If you have chronic or intermittent insomnia, what if you didn't think of it in terms of dis-ease? What if you knew for sure it was a temporary condition that you could use as an opening to new awareness? We all know the sleeplessness of grief, stress, and crisis. Doesn't it make sense we are vigilant at those times and less likely to sleep? What if nature gave us those hours to process and to heal?

Maybe your sleeplessness is not just your normal, but a mystical invitation to transformation. Of course, I'm not a medical doctor, and this isn't medical advice. It's metaphysical advice.

In the night, the third eye opens, and we see what we cannot see by the light of day.

Notes

Insomnia is a pretty tough form of resistance. It might start out as a reaction to stress or a particularly difficult phase of life, but it can grow a life of its own and then, no matter what we do, sleep won't come. And the more we think about not sleeping while we are lying there trying very hard to fall asleep, the less sleep we get. Thich Nhat Hahn says,

"Our true home is the present moment. To live in the present moment is a miracle."

That would include the moments we hate; the sleepless ones we want to escape.

WRITING PROMPT

Dream up a perfect way to spend the night. Who do you spend the night with? (It's a fantasy, make it good!) Let it be ideal, idyllic, blissful.

MIDNIGHT PAGES

MIDNIGHT PAGES

MIDNIGHT PAGES

EXCIEO

Excieo is to rouse or stir. When waking up in the middle of the night, we try not to allow ourselves to rouse too much. The more movement, the more thoughts that pile on, the less likely we are to get back to sleep. We dread having to get up to go to the bathroom in the "wee" hours of the morning. We know then we will lie awake fixated on how we can't get to sleep and what it will mean for the following day. Every thought that gets in the way of relaxing, every hour that goes by, we are losing the precious rest we crave. Maybe you know the desperation of counting how many hours you'd get if you fell asleep *right now*. It's a perfect example of the saying *what we resist persists*.

Notes

*In this immeasurable darkness, be the power
that rounds your senses in this magic ring, the
sense of their mysterious encounter.*
–Rainer Maria Rilke

Instead of resenting your wakefulness, imagine that this is the night your muse finally shows up. Tonight is the night you draft that electrifying story you always knew was in you. You get up and decide to try your hand at something new and before dawn breaks, realize that you're good at it. Maybe you will finally dive into writing your memoir and discover the meaning of your life. Who knows, it could be that your future reader finds herself in the very same pages where you found you.

Many a book is like a key to unknown
chambers within the castle of one's own self.
–Franz Kafka

WRITING PROMPT

Is your muse a witch or a faery or something else? Does she take dictation? If she were a waitress in a 1970s diner, what would you order? What would she bring you? Write her a letter. Give her some attitude. What do you want from that witch?

MIDNIGHT PAGES

MIDNIGHT PAGES

MAGICAL WRITING PRACTICES

If you are a mystic, metaphysician, or other magical being, you may have even grander intentions for your night writing. Why not? You can allow night messengers to deliver exactly what you need to start or finish your book. You can become a channel or do some automatic writing by getting in the right frame of mind, putting your fingers on the keyboard, and opening to spiritual guidance. You might write an entire book that way. (I swear I have, judging from the words on the page the morning after, few of which I remember putting there.)

Y ou could seek the solutions to the riddles of your life or explore the resistance that plagues you with the help of spirit guides. I know many people who use writing for this very purpose. They write to know themselves, and sometimes they get help from interested others.

And as to me, I know nothing else but miracles. –Walt Whitman

WRITING PROMPT

Formulate a list of ten ideas. Then pick one and write it at the top of a page. Imagine that you shift a few inches away from the center of your keyboard or notebook and Infinite Intelligence moves into your seat. Allow what wants to be written about your idea (which is your writing prompt to Infinite Intelligence) to take form on the page.

1.

2.

3.

4.

5.

6.

7.

8.

9.

10.

MIDNIGHT PAGES

MIDNIGHT PAGES

MIDNIGHT PAGES

NIGHT FANCIES

Fancies are imaginative, fun, easy, festive, light-hearted thoughts. Since you're interested in writing, it would be good to tell you that I teach people how to write (and live) from the path of least resistance, which is about following joy and not struggle.[9] That principle underlies this entire book. Yes, we all face resistance: writer's block, feeling stuck, self-criticism and self-doubt, and more. The first step on a path of joy is accepting what is. My advice is never to go to war with any form of resistance. Not your procrastination, writer's block, overwhelm, or whatever else keeps you from writing. Resistance, however it shows up, is a doorway into the place where your true inspiration lies.

Notes

Resistance is like insomnia in that they both seem to hunker down when we fight them. But if we can see them as a symptom of something deeper, then our healing, metamorphosis, or transformation is at hand.

By believing passionately in something that still does not exist, we create it. The nonexistent is whatever we have not sufficiently desired. –Franz Kafka

When it comes to resistance, especially writer's block, you'll be glad to know that being up at night heightens it—makes it even more annoying, frustrating, louder, insistent, and, therefore, easier to see. And now that you see it, you have a chance to start a conversation, make friends.

Whether your resistance shows up as physical symptoms or haunting, ancient, negative thoughts of self-criticism and worry or as behaviors and habits like putting things off, resistance has a voice. If you could back off your urgency to fix it and stop judging yourself for a few nights, you might find out what it wants to say. Slow down. Be curious why you're not writing, why you're not sleeping. Just listen. It's not only your writing that will open up and spill its secrets.

You do not need to leave your room. Remain sitting at your table and listen. Do not even listen, simply wait, be quiet, still and solitary. The world will freely offer itself to you to be unmasked, it has no choice, it will roll in ecstasy at your feet. –Franz Kafka

WRITING PROMPT

You can experiment with what it feels like to dump thoughts onto paper so you don't have to cart them around with you anymore. Imagine how much room that will clear up in your head for more creative things. List all the things that get in the way of starting, working on, or finishing your book (or any other creative project).

1. _____

2. _____

3. _____

4. _____

5. _____

6. _____

7. _____

8. _____

9. _____

10. _____

11. _____

12.

13.

14.

15.

16.

17.

18.

19.

20.

21.

22.

23.

24.

25.

Night is a time of rigor but also of mercy. There are truths which one can see only when it's dark. –Isaac Bashevis Singer

MIDNIGHT PAGES

MIDNIGHT PAGES

MIDNIGHT PAGES

GRIFFONAGE

How can you clear your mind for sleep, to rest and relax at the close of the day? If you struggle to shut your brain off, Griffonage might help. The word means "illegible scrawl," and I've turned it into a writing practice. You can use it before bed to clear your head or before you write.

Take up your pen and write on a loose leaf piece of paper without looking. Close your eyes or stare into space or make it dark enough in the room that you can barely see the paper. You aren't necessarily writing recognizable words, and if at the end, you can't read it, that's okay. Just scribble. The writing itself is the goal.

With Griffonage, you can't judge whether it is good or not. Let yourself write freely, with abandon, for the joy of your hand flying across the page, writing absolutely nothing of value, note, or worth. Huzzah! I am writing illegible scrawl, and it feels wonderful, and someday all these meaningless words will be replaced with gems and jewels, and this will have been the place where it all began, the writing that primed the pump and started the flow, and now I am in the flow, I am flowing. I am the flow.

Once you're finished, tear the page up and throw it away. A key part of Griffonage is nonattachment to the outcome. Don't skip this step.

MIDNIGHT PAGES

MIDNIGHT PAGES

MIDNIGHT PAGES

MIDNIGHT OIL

"It smells of the candle"[10] meant someone had been writing at night, burning the midnight tallow. Now we say we burn oil. Same feeling.

Burning the midnight oil isn't the same as moonlighting, which is working a secret or second job after your daytime, full-time one. Burning the midnight oil is studying or working on a project you're passionate about. It's urgent, necessary. You are driven, highly motivated. It might feel uncomfortable or unfamiliar, even pressurized, but it doesn't feel bad.

Burning the midnight oil is high vibration. It is converting creativity into words or artwork. It incinerates brain cells and has the energy of combustion or alchemy. We are turning one thing into another, and the fuel is our inner fire combined with the night.

Sometimes it happens naturally. We stay up because there's momentum, possibly a deadline. We are excited. The inner urge says, You've got to get this down! Don't lose the train of thought! Don't let the muse get away! We feel a touch of panic that if we lay it aside, we will forget—not just the words, but the feeling, the juice. It's as if we have a window of opportunity, and it's closing. We have to squeeze through before it does.

Even if the words aren't flowing yet, we're inspired, energized to the point where we couldn't sleep if we tried. We are lit up from within. Who needs sleep?

How did it get so late so soon? –Dr. Seuss

Maybe your beloved worries about you. It's hard to get non-writers, linear thinkers, or anyone who isn't in that zone to understand. "It's not good for you," they say. "You need your sleep. Come to bed." But it's the last thing on our mind, which is racing with ideas the way our fingers are racing over the page or keyboard, full of words that want to spill out. Hurry up, a voice urges. You're on fire! Yes, we're burning the midnight oil.

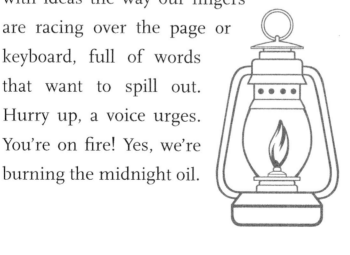

WRITING PROMPT

Write like your hair's on fire.
Burn, baby, burn.

MIDNIGHT PAGES

MIDNIGHT PAGES

MIDNIGHT PAGES

MIDNIGHT PAGES

IN THE STILL OF THE NIGHT

When I can't sleep, I read. That's good for a writer, but it is addictive. And if you have a book (especially one with a deadline), it's a distraction. But who hasn't stayed up all night turning pages? So here's a challenge: don't read.

> *Books are a narcotic.*
> –Franz Kafka

Don't read. At least not for a few weeks, at least not until your book is done or the key plot points are out and on paper. The writing prompt on the next page might help. It lets you at least think about reading books.

WRITING PROMPT

Imagine a library, shelves full of
books pertaining to your life or your
writing project. One is calling you.
What is it called? What's on the
cover? What does it say?

MIDNIGHT PAGES

MIDNIGHT PAGES

THE MUSIC OF THE NIGHT

If there weren't so many restrictions, permissions, and costs associated with using song lyrics, this book would be full of references to music about the night. It is enormously tempting to grab a song or two and take my chances. (But I won't.) You already know there is something in the air (most) nights, and the darkness sharpens our senses and stirs the imagination.

Notes

Through the years, music has told us that nighttime is the right time for making love, finding romance, and getting jiggy. It's ideal for late night radio, dancing, twisting in the street, walking in the moonlight, and meeting the perfect someone. *If you think you know which songs (and bands, singers, shows, and songwriters) I am alluding to, come to the Midnight Pages Facebook group and play my ongoing contest for who can come up with the most obscure, night-leaning, night-idealizing songs.*

Here would be the perfect place for lyrics. Too bad.

WRITING PROMPT

Pick a line from a song about the night and write a one-page story about it. Be sure it includes mushrooms, toadstools, or lichen.

MIDNIGHT PAGES

MIDNIGHT PAGES

MIDNIGHT PAGES

EVENSONG

Evensong is an ancient service of worship that gives thanks to God for the day past and asks protection from the gathering dusk and all the things that threaten during the night, including ghostly foes, bad dreams, fears, dangers, fantasies, and "pollution." You can guess what that is. During evensong, you will hear psalms, prayers, and canticles, which are sung or chanted.

Vespers, from the Latin word for evening, also means services of prayer, songs, and readings conducted around sunset. Compline, another name for a similar sacred liturgy, occurs an hour or so later, right before bed.

Notes

The "offices" of the church (liturgies, readings, prayers, songs, or chants) are scheduled around the clock to help the faithful stay attentive to God all day and night long, and probably to keep them so busy they didn't have time to sin or to "pollute" themselves.

In Judaism, there are fixed hours for prayer, and like Moslems and Christians, for the same reason: to keep God forefront in adherents' minds. The evening prayers of Islam include Maghrib which is performed after sunset and Isha, offered at night. The schedule for the right prayer time is very specific and determined by astronomers' reading of the stars. Nowadays, of course, there's an app to help you keep on track with your Salah times.

If you never heard of liturgy or Isha, canonical hours, or offices of the church, I'm sure you've heard this bedtime prayer for children. It says pretty much the same thing as all the grown-up vespers, prayers, and petitions do:

> *Now I lay me down to sleep*
> *I pray dear Lord my soul to keep*
> *And if I die before I wake*
> *I pray dear Lord my soul to take.*

WRITING PROMPT

Write yourself a bedtime prayer
or canticle (song or chant) to give
thanks for the day and ask for
"illumination" in the night. Address
it to God/Goddess as you know them
or to your Higher Self.

MIDNIGHT PAGES

MIDNIGHT PAGES

NIGHT SHIFT

Twenty-first century spirituality seems very busy. We start with miracle mornings, morning pages, lemon water. Then, we meditate or do our sun salutations followed by exercise, celery juice, reciting our affirmations, and writing our intentions. First thing in the morning? All that? It'd be noon before I started my regular day. Compared to us, weren't ancient people more attuned to the rhythms of seasons, of night and day, more in touch with the Divine? More peaceful and prayerful? I'm idealizing. Life was even more perilous than it is now, and if people prayed, it was probably in desperation.

Night is a tranquil time to follow a spiritual routine. It helps us wind down to write, meditate, contemplate when the world is still and there are no demands being made on us. By the time we are finished, we are ready for sleep and set to dream meaningful dreams.

What is more conducive to wisdom than the night? –St. Cyril of Jerusalem

Midnight Pages can help you establish a rhythm of your own, reflective, creative, and quiet, while you are enveloped in the illuminating night.

At a weekend with Deepak Chopra at Omega Institute in Rhinebeck, New York, over twenty years ago, he instructed us to recapitulate our day before bed and recapitulate our dreams when we wake up in the morning. Yes, there were also numerous meditations, practices, and even dietary recommendations we were supposed to follow. Busy, busy. But the recapitulation practice stuck with me.

Let sleep not come upon thy languid eyes
Before each daily action thou has scanned;
What's done amiss, what's done,
what's left undone;
From first to last examine all,
And then Blame what is wrong,
in what is right
Rejoice.
—Attributed to Pythagoras

WRITING PROMPT

Recapitulate your day as
though it was the end of a
novel or the last paragraph
in your memoir.

MIDNIGHT PAGES

MIDNIGHT PAGES

HALLUCINAR

Hallucinar means to dream. It's a risk of sleeping—that we will dream unpleasantly. You know the feeling of waking up from a dream or nightmare and feeling haunted. It's unforgettable, and you can't get back to sleep. Maybe part of the problem is you're afraid if you do, the dream will repeat. If the dream comes near morning, it can color your day. You have to talk yourself out of the bad mood it leaves, to remind yourself you're not really angry or in danger or crawling through a spider-invested alley on your belly.

Notes

For anyone plagued by nightmares that wake them up in a cold sweat (or even the kind of dream that leaves a weird taste in your mouth), it's a real thing. We tell a child "it was only a dream," but we know better. The thing of it is, we have "daymares" too—anxiety attacks, panic, long spells of depression, sadness, despair. Often, the bad dreams of the night are actually easier to dispel than the ones that haunt us during the day. If you have ever experienced repeated negative thoughts, habitual worries, or times when you couldn't get something out of your mind—and of course, you have—you know what I mean.

Who looks outside, dreams. Who looks inside, awakes. –Carl Jung

My dreams are as real as my daily life. I can't tell you which I feel more deeply. It's a big part of our earthly existence, these dreaming hours (probably around two hours each night). Who knows? Dreams might be putting us in touch with a part of ourselves from another lifetime or a parallel life. Why miss it? It might help us banish the habitual daymares that keep us stuck.

We can train ourselves to remember our dreams, to act intentionally within them, and to mine them for the gold and guidance they offer.

Deep into that darkness peering, long I stood there, wondering, fearing, doubting, dreaming... –Edgar Allan Poe

WRITING PROMPT

Use your nightmare as a writing prompt. When one wakes you up, turn on a light and write down as much as you can remember. This will give you clarity on what it might mean but will also diffuse its power. We usually don't remember dreams in their entirety. They are, at least in some parts, fragmentary. There will be gaps, and you will remember how one thing morphed into another. As you write, let it break up. Intentionally, let there be lots of room on the page between the words, between the lines. The dream spreads out thin, until you can't get lost in it anymore. Soon, it's just words on a page. Tear the page out, rip it up, throw it out the window as an offering to the night.

...what if you added to that, it's going to be okay no matter what? –Joanna Lundenbaum

MIDNIGHT PAGES

MIDNIGHT PAGES

MIDNIGHT PAGES

SWEVEN

Sweven is an archaic word for dream or vision. We were talking a moment ago about nightmares, so here's a tip you might want to try. When I was young, I discovered a key to preventing nightmares. For me, they are mostly triggered by things I see. Things I hear or experience don't seem as powerful to inspire bad dreams but pictures, visuals, and indelible images definitely are. Now, as soon as I see something that has the potential to bring on a nightmare, I slap my thigh and say, "Oh, great! Now I'll have a nightmare about that!" It acts as a ward (a form of magic) against a bad dream.

You can use the same incantation or turn it into a positive statement instead, like so: I am free of nightmares, no matter what I see (or hear or experience)! Say it like you mean it. You can use any gesture of banishment. I slap my thigh. You could clap your hands. It's called "anchoring," and it comes from neurolinguistic programming. The key is to catch the trigger, whether it's a sight, experience, movie, or a weird torn toenail on your right foot. The second you think it might be nightmare fodder, ward it off! Feel to your bones that you're free of it and so it is.

WRITING PROMPT

If you were the author of your own nightmares (and you are), who is the hero best able to save you? If you had the authority (and you do), to decide how it all works out, what is the powerful, overcoming moment of your dream? What is the tool of your freedom, the solution to the struggle? What is the "safe word" you can use to wake yourself up from a dream before things get too terrifying?

MIDNIGHT PAGES

MIDNIGHT PAGES

MIDNIGHT PAGES

HALUNICOR

Halucinor is to wonder. We can wonder all day about our life's purpose or why we can't reach our dreams. We can perseverate over our failings and wonder what we are doing wrong. But there is a repository of wisdom that can help us get out of the loop of our thinking. It comes from a wiser, deeper part of us, and we can learn to access it through dreaming.

Dreams can be messengers from your deepest self, from memory, from your subconscious. They help you process and connect experiences and events. They arise with symbols from the cosmic unconscious, that wellspring of images, archetypes, and meanings beyond our individual selves.

The night brings counsel. –16th century proverb

Notes

There are entire libraries of books about dream symbolism and interpretation, lucid dreaming, and so much more. For the purposes of this book, I want to offer one writing practice. It consists of three steps:

1. Write down the dream in a few sentences.

2. List all the individual features of the dream.

3. Every aspect of the dream represents you. Now, retell the dream with that in mind.

Here's an example:

1. Summarize: There were doors opening onto a narrow, tight hall, and I had to walk down the hall past them all. Some were scary, and I didn't want to go near them. Others

had golden light spilling out of them. I started to walk, and a cat appeared. I picked it up. It was warm in my arms. We went toward the light at the end of the hall.

2. List the individual features of the dream: Narrow hall, some open doors with light pouring out and others I didn't want to pass because I was scared, a warm cat, light at the end of the hall.

3. Interpretation: I am narrow. Inside of me are places I don't want to go near because I am scared. Inside, there are places in me that light is spilling out of. I am like a cat, which is warm, has nine lives, sees in the dark. I am walking toward the light.

I'd take it to mean I am being narrow-minded about something. There are light and dark aspects of me. But I have sweet warmth (the cat) I can take with me; I can see in the dark (cat again), and I have nine lives—plenty of chances. I am walking toward the light at the end of the hall.

WRITING PROMPT

Dream interpretation: Summarize your dream briefly. Next, list the key features of the dream. Finally, assuming every feature of the dream represents you, interpret from that viewpoint.

MIDNIGHT PAGES

 # MIDNIGHT PAGES

If you've been wrestling with a problem, maybe worry isn't what's keeping you up. Maybe it's the solution.

LUNACY

The full moon packs a wallop. Her cycles impact bodies of water like ours, raise up our tides. They make storms more wild. Emergency rooms fill up, and people go a little crazy. We feel "off," a little drugged, tired, or elated. According to etymology.com, the word lunatic dates from the thirteenth century and referred to "periodic insanity dependent on the changes of the moon." From Late Latin *lunaticus* "moon-struck," in Old English *monseoc* "lunatic," literally "moon-sick."

Even if you feel completely ordinary regardless of the moon phase, look at the moon shadows around your room and see how they change throughout the month. What do you notice?

WRITING PROMPT

Next full moon, try writing only by
its light. Let the moonlight inspire
you and deliver timeless and eternal
messages just for you. If you do it,
you'll see how magical it is. You'll
have a night you will remember.
After all, it's not every night but once
every hallowed, sacred month...

MIDNIGHT PAGES

MIDNIGHT PAGES

NIGHT TRANCE

S it and take a few deep breaths. Listen to the night. If a window is open, even better. Crickets, cicadas, wind, rain, the rustling of papers in the street, sirens, foraging raccoons or rats in the garbage can. Listen to your breathing, the furnace coming on, the water pinging in the pipes, the house settling, someone snoring down the hall. After a while, the sounds are hypnotic. They go where they will, and you follow.

Once you are in a reverie, a dwam, a slight stupor, pick up your pen and write. Bring to mind your characters, the chapter you left off in your memoir, whatever it is you are working on. Stay in this state of somewhat-unconsciousness. Write.

DWAMMING (WRITING IN A HAZY STATE OF MIND)

WRITING PROMPT

I believe in the magic of lists. They've proven themselves over and over; they have a power to make manifest the things we want and intend to accomplish. Try it.

Make a list of fifty ways you can make more friends or fifty ways you can end your novel. How about fifty sentences you can put in the mouth of your protagonist to show her street-wise panache. Or fifty possible solutions to a problem you've been wrestling with. When the list gets hard, you're getting closer; you're on the verge of getting help from your subconscious, your Higher Self, divine help. Up will pop a crazy idea, a laughable, useful idea, an insight, a thing you might want to try. An insight that'll blast open a creative crack in your resistance. It might seem unrealistic at best, but it'll shake loose some other ideas, and resistance will fade away into a flurry of writing, creativity, dreaming, problem solving.

1. _____
2. _____
3. _____
4. _____
5. _____
6. _____
7. _____
8. _____
9. _____
10. _____
11. _____
12. _____
13. _____
14. _____
15. _____
16. _____
17. _____
18. _____
19. _____

20. _____
21. _____
22. _____
23. _____
24. _____
25. _____
26. _____
27. _____
28. _____
29. _____
30. _____
31. _____
32. _____
33. _____
34. _____
35. _____

36. _____
37. _____
38. _____
39. _____
40. _____
41. _____
42. _____
43. _____
44. _____
45. _____
46. _____
47. _____
48. _____
49. _____
50. _____

MIDNIGHT PAGES

MIDNIGHT PAGES

A NEAR-SLEEP
EXPERIENCE

The mental state of "I can't concentrate at this hour!" is perfect for theta-brainwave writing or, as I call it, Sleepy Writing. Theta is the state of mind right before sleep or just after waking; you can also feel that liminal state during and after daydreaming and meditation. The ego steps aside, the pen moves, you don't know how or who's writing.

Sleepy is a good state for writing but not if you're frustrated by your wakefulness. Anxious brainwaves interrupt the creative flow and then we can't access intuition or inspiration.

What I learned about theta brainwaves is on that wavelength, we can "reprogram" our subconscious mind, undoing the conditioning put there before we were seven years old. In childhood, we are little sponges soaking up information about the world and ourselves. We digest "facts" about our abilities, worth, appearance, and potential without question, and that programming

is often what keeps us from achieving what we want in life. It's the reason that no matter how hard we try, we seem to hit a wall. It's why we aren't happy with ourselves even when we do get what we think we want. *Who was it that said, "Give me the child until he is seven, and I will show you the man"?*

Personally, I've not yet been deprogrammed, but I do slip into a cool writing vibe in sleepy state. Go ahead and see what happens for you. The closer you are to unconsciousness, the less self-consciousness and self-judgement you will have. The deeper into this altered state, the farther away your rational, critical mind.

Notes

You can wake up early or stay up late but wait until you're feeling sleepy. Then instead of lying down to fall asleep, prop yourself up and just be in a state of fuzzy consciousness. You're not concentrating; you're letting your subconscious take over. You are detached from evaluating your writing. Don't worry if it's good or bad or whether you sound smart or literary.

Good ideas live here in the subconscious— plots and characters' back stories, poems, and memoir memories. Who knows, maybe they actually were planted before you were seven when the world was magical, and there were angels watching over your bed while you slept.

WRITING PROMPT

If you're like me, up most of the night, that theta state—halfway between awake and dreamland—might not come until the afternoon. It doesn't matter what time of day, try writing whenever you feel sleepy, in that state where you know you could fall off if you laid down. See what part of your brain is awake when you're half asleep. Practice it here...

MIDNIGHT PAGES

# MIDNIGHT PAGES

MIDNIGHT PAGES

DARK NIGHT OF THE SOUL

The phrase "dark night of the soul" was coined by St. John of the Cross in the sixteenth century about the journey toward God. The church used it to mean a spiritual crisis, but when I read it, it seemed more like a love poem about how the soul moves from desire for God to knowing God. That journey does have its ups and downs. But today it implies a dark time, rock bottom before what we hope is transformation. You've probably had these nights, when the monsters you confront come from the drama and turmoil of being human: sickness, addiction, loneliness, abandonment, crises of faith and confidence. A dark night of the soul may be what's keeping you awake right now. Tonight, you might feel ragged, exhausted, desperate. Maybe you have the empty gnawing sensation of hunger that comes from lack of sleep, different from ordinary hunger, and insatiable. And after nights of this, you might be spending your days feeling wasted.

May your transformation come. May this night or this insomnia or this condition of your soul be your moment of spiritual transformation.

In the seventeenth century, theologian Thomas Fuller wrote that it's always darkest before the dawn, and even though you might feel like your light will never come, remember:

The dark night of the soul comes just before revelation. –Joseph Campbell

WRITING PROMPT

Write about the earliest dark night of the soul you can remember. Maybe it happened before you were even old enough to call it that.

MIDNIGHT PAGES

MIDNIGHT PAGES

MIDNIGHT PAGES

A SPELL OF WAKEFULNESS

Some people love the night and crave it. Why feel conflicted just because eight hours is today's recommendation? What feels good to you is good for you. Again, not medical advice. Metaphysical advice.

I wonder how many eight hours of uninterrupted sleep our cave-dwelling ancestors got in a week. Especially the person at the mouth of the cave, watching the ancient night for monsters and nocturnal carnivores. He wasn't sleeping all through the night either. Think about how evolutionarily wired your sleep pattern is. Did anyone in that cave fall into utter, blissful, ignorant rest? Doubt it.

Notes

Contrary to common belief, our earliest ancestors may not have instinctively slept after dark. The custom of reserving nighttime for rest, some psychologists now surmise, evolved gradually among prehistoric peoples. Only with the passage of time did these first generations learn to sleep away the dangers of darkness by resting in caves, sheltered from foraging predators. –A Roger Ekirch

So, do I think that sleeping through the night is an unnatural waste of time? Am I suggesting that you should try to stay up all night? No but I do think we should listen to our inner guidance and always, always investigate what we are experiencing. When it comes to sleeplessness, if I was worried about it I'd ask, why did my insomnia arise when it did? Did it accompany some significant loss or change? I'd believe what my body, heart and soul was telling me. I like to see the symptom, (for example being awake when I want to be asleep), as a doorway into the unknown, deepest reaches of myself. Whether you are thirteen or eighty-three you do have some pretty fascinating deep reaches, in case you were wondering. Go plumb them! Night is the perfect time for it.

So, the bottom line is, if you're up, be up. Don't waste the time feeling miserable about it. If you're up, there is a reason and finding out what the reason is might solve a day-time problem or help you get back to sleep once it's figured out. Who knows? You might be guided to your destiny, your life's purpose or to your deepest inner wisdom. If you're awake stop trying hard to be asleep. Listen to the voices of the night and expect to hear something *good*.

Everything is pointing the way, always. You are here for a reason and the entire Universe conspires every day to tell you what that reason is. Sometimes we're just too busy or distracted during the day to hear it. So, good news! You're up in the middle of the night with ears wide open. Make use of the time and listen.

WRITING PROMPT

Do you believe you have inner wisdom? You do. Most of us go through life without ever consulting it though. Tonight, with your pen in hand, have a conversation with your inner wise person. Maybe your sage is Wonder Woman, and she can tell you about your evil foe. Or you'll find Yoda and have to decipher his odd way of speaking. Or your wise one might not have a face at all but just a message. Here are some questions to ask him or her or them.

- Where is my buried treasure?

- Am I cocoon or butterfly?

- All the signs of my life are pointing at something. What am I missing?

MIDNIGHT PAGES

MIDNIGHT PAGES

MIDNIGHT PAGES

NOCTURNALIS

Nocturnalis means belonging to the night. As I mentioned, I couldn't find many happy insomniacs on social media. But when I started asking around, I found plenty of people willing to confess to working, writing, and communing with the Universe late at night. Best of all, they liked it. Tova said, "The daytime obstructs the Universe; it distracts me. I have a clearer view of God, and I can be more introspective at night. It's easier to reflect."

Night is the oldest path to the human psyche.
—A. Roger Ekirch

Myriam, who had expressed a preference for morning, said, "You're going to laugh, but I realized I really do like to work on the fun, creative jobs at night."

My story is that last year, I knew I was supposed to write a book, my first piece of fiction. I boiled and bubbled about it but didn't write. Then I started developing symptoms. Then the book hijacked my sleep. Yes, I always have a hard time falling and staying asleep, but this was full-on, up all night. But the night started pointed out sources to me. First was the poem Don't Sleep by Rumi, set to music and pictures and read aloud on YouTube. More breadcrumbs out of the forest followed. It felt as if the Universe was laying out the contents of the book. I figured those thoughts would always be there. So I procrastinated. Then I got sick. I was afraid it was something serious. What if it was? Would I ever get the chance to write it? Panic did not help the writing process. My neck started hurting and so did my throat. If you know anything about chakras, that's the fifth—the seat of self-expression. I decided to focus on feeling better. Taking the pressure off myself about the book.

Then one afternoon on the way to pick up my son, I was sitting at a traffic light and was rear-ended. Twice. The driver actually backed up and hit me again. Then he drove off without so much as a wave.

Just a few days before I'd had a premonition of this very thing.

All of these: the illness, the sleeplessness, the precognition the accident, and my fifth chakra alarm bells were conspiring to tell me something. The thought kept recurring: if I only had a few months to live, what would I be doing? I knew the answer; I got up and wrote.

When the book was done a few weeks later, I slept peacefully for many nights. But I missed the messages, even the scary ones, which had conspired to show me what I had to do.

All the events and feelings you experience are conspiring every single day to guide you too. Are you paying attention?

I created a process to help you interpret your messages, the signs and symptoms of your life. I posted it on thebellywitch.com and themidnightpages.com.

Now I created a process to help you interpret your messages, the signs and symptoms of your life. I posted it on *thebellywitch.com* and *themidnightpages.com*.

WRITING PROMPT

What if your symptoms were signs of something deeper: your creativity calling, your deepest desires, as yet unfulfilled, nagging? What if being up at night is literally your wake-up call?

MIDNIGHT PAGES

MIDNIGHT PAGES

GODDESS OF THE NIGHT

The primordial goddess of the night is Nyx (Greek) or Nox (Roman) or Nut (Egyptian). Nótt is the Norse (female) personification of night. In the Vedic tradition, which predates Hinduism, the epitome of darkness and the personification of night is the goddess Ratri. Then there's also Achlys, the Greco-Roman Goddess of the Eternal Night (and really, isn't that the one we fear the most, the eternal night, the one we don't wake up from?).

Sleep, delicious and profound, the very counterfeit of death. –Homer, The Odyssey

You don't hear a lot about Nyx/Nox/ Nut, obviously the same goddess with slightly different names, but as with Goddess of Night Ratri, she is more ancient than the pantheons of gods with whom we are most familiar.

Goddess of the Night, whatever we call her, predates the dawn of time; since before there was anything, there was the roiling stew of creation where all possibility lay. Those waters were dark, potent, containing the very ingredients of all things that could be made. She was called Chaos and her daughter was Nyx, Goddess of the Night.

Fear of the dark is as old as the words, "Let there be light."

In the Hebrew Bible (the Christian's Old Testament), the god Yahweh takes as his first official act the subduing of Chaos, the goddess of the primordial deep. In the bible story, it sounds like the forces of good (light, God) subdue the forces of evil, disorder, and darkness (Chaos, the source of all creation). But it's a triumph of God subduing Goddess and those who served her.

In some mystery cults, it was believed that everything begins in the dark. "Let there be light," says the book of Genesis, and Goddess of Darkness, from whom all things come, is banished.

In the beginning God created the heavens and earth. The earth was without form and void, and darkness was upon the face of the deep; and the Spirit of God was moving over the face of the waters. And God said, "Let there be light." And God saw that the light was good; and God separated the light from the darkness. God called the light Day, and the darkness he called Night. –Genesis 1: 1-5

Nyx, daughter of Chaos, is a charioteer, drawn by a pair of black horses or bulls. Bulls were associated with Goddess in the ancient civilizations of Old Europe and the Mediterranean.

When Zeus came on the scene, even he feared Nyx, since she was more powerful and more ancient than he. Nyx frightened nearly everyone. She brought the curtain of darkness down over the world each night, terrifying ancient peoples who didn't have the advantage of artificial light and central heat. On a moonless night, who wouldn't worry that dawn might never come, that we'd be swallowed up by the night or the creatures who moved around in it. Over time, Nyx became associated with negative dark forces: war, death, and famine and not only the creative darkness of soil, ocean, nighttime, and sleep.

Coincidentally, as I was working on this section, my Tarot card draw was of the Charioteer and Nut, the Goddess of the nighttime sky, stars, and cosmos. Again, the Universe winked.

WRITING PROMPT

Write a myth or a symbolic story about the moon, the night, creation, mystery. Use the gods and goddesses you know or make some up.

MIDNIGHT PAGES

MIDNIGHT PAGES

EVIGLIO

Eviglio is to be fully alert. If you watch the night go by, alert to every moving minute, it will absolutely feel like a grind. But if you look for inner messages, meanings, inspiration, then worlds unfold. Lessons from your life suddenly become clear, even obvious. The ahas of the night might not make much sense in the light of day, but it doesn't matter. Still, you'll be changed, shifted—different. And if you take the time to write during your late night vigils, reading back over what you've written the next day may be a revelation.

Notes

If you are wide awake regularly in the middle of the night (whether you enjoy that or not), do you ever wonder if your sleep patterns are genetic or something even deeper? It could be that we, the sleepless, come from a long line of inspiration-seekers or shamans. We have been the priests, witches, healers, the ones who stay up late keeping other people's secrets and offering mystical potions that shouldn't be handled in the light of day. Maybe over the course of many lifetimes you met desperate souls under the cover of darkness to dispense wisdom and direction.

Maybe you're the descendent of a keeper of the watchtower, a sentry on the hill, a man at the drawbridge, protecting the castle through the eternal night. Whatever your day job, you are still vigilant. Why did the night pick you? What does the night show you?

WRITING PROMPT

What to ask (and answer) instead of, "Why am I up at three o'clock again?"

What does 3 a.m. have to tell me? What's trying to be remembered? Who's here with a message? What do I need to know tonight? What wants to be created? What am I being called to create? What wants to be let go? What wants to be forgiven? What wants to come out?

MIDNIGHT PAGES

MIDNIGHT PAGES

MIDNIGHT PAGES

SURGERE

Surgere means "arise." It makes me think about waking up as resurrection, coming back to life from the sleep of the dead. There aren't many examples of resurrection in history, but when they do appear, it's usually for a reason, right? So many insomnia programs promise effortless sleep. What if you are blessed with effortless opportunities for waking up, resurrection, and new life?

After trying some of those aforementioned insomnia programs, I realized I don't want to give up my sleep pattern. It is a part of me, a chance to be alone, to find myself, to hear myself think. Every time I wake up, I am resurrected with a new inspiration, a new chance to create and make meaning out of my life.

Notes

If the night presents me a problem, I know it arrives with the solution. Every time a nightmare shows up, there is a message. Instead of fighting the messenger (the night, the sleeplessness), what if we looked for the gift, the message that comes with it? What if we constantly ask for the meaning, the direction, the answers to our deepest questions? Ask the dark, ask the spirits, even ask the things that scare you—the nightmare that woke you. What is the meaning of this? Then write down what you hear.

WRITING PROMPT

Maybe in some other lifetime you were a shepherd watching over her flock by night or the stopgap, the last man standing between invading armies and the king. Falling asleep would mean his downfall and probably your death, whether by the enemy's hand or his when he discovered how you failed him. This was the kingdom you were sworn to protect, and you cannot permit it to be overrun.

Tell the story of how you came to be responsible for the king, the castle, the village, the house where your people slept. What made you the person they trusted to protect them through the long, dark, dangerous night?

MIDNIGHT PAGES

MIDNIGHT PAGES

MIDNIGHT PAGES

THE FAIRY TALES
OF SLEEP

Sleeping Beauty, whose name is actually Briar Rose, is cursed by an evil stepmother. When she is fifteen years old, she pricks her finger and falls into a thousand-year sleep, a spell that can only be broken by true love's kiss. To prevent this from happening and to deepen the spell, the sleep will also come over the entire castle, the queen, and the king.

Snow White eats the cursed apple given to her by the evil, jealous queen. She, too, will only be awakened by the kiss of a prince. Surrounded by friendly dwarfs, she sleeps in the woods until he comes.

In the story of the Princess and the Pea, a queen wants to ensure that her son will marry a true princess and not a poseur. Princesses are delicate beings, and so the queen places a hard, dry pea under a pile of mattresses, knowing that an ordinary girl would never be kept awake by a tiny pea. Of course, the princess tosses and turns all night.

In the story of Hansel and Gretel, the two children try to escape the evil crone in the dark of night. Because they would lose their way in the dark, they lay white pebbles in the path, knowing the moonlight will reflect off them and show the way out of the forest. That's my favorite image for teaching and coaching writers and other seekers. There are always glowing pebbles if you stay up and look for them.

WRITING PROMPT

It's a fun quest to discover stories with sleep and nighttime at their core. Come to think of it, night plays a starring role in most fairy tales. Search online, get inspired, then write yourself a fable, a fairy tale, or a legend about the night. If you're writing a memoir, give us a chapter about the nights in your life. Is there a theme to your evenings? Is there a heroic overcoming your fairy tale hero or heroine has to tell?

MIDNIGHT PAGES

MIDNIGHT PAGES

NOCTURN

A nocturn is a prayer said before daybreak in the "offices" (prayer schedule) of the church. It is not to be confused with nocturne, which means music evocative of the night or a painting of a night scene.

The church considered night a time of temptation (known to the secular world as "having a good time under the cover of darkness") as well as a metaphor for suffering. Folks who believe such things probably felt truly relieved when it came time to pray these near-daybreak prayers. Soon, the sun would come up, and they would be free from their perilous vigil. What the heck were they watching for? They were exhorted to watch for the coming of God, who could arrive at any time. They were expected to be ready.

Watch ye, therefore, for you know not when
the lord of the house cometh; at even,
or at midnight, or at the cock-crowing,
or in the morning.
–The Christian Gospel of Mark 8: 3-5

I read recently that the church considered night a time of contemplation and peace, an opportunity for people to pray and reflect.[11] But the religious images of danger, suffering, sin, and death stick out much more boldly in my mind.

If you've ever been up all night suffering, watching for something that never comes, struggling with depression, facing mortality, or trying to make a terrible decision, you know what a daybreak prayer might include. Maybe you've been up all hours, in pain, wrestling with your demons, experiencing your own dark night of the soul. Thinking of the dawn as a break from the struggle, what do you want to see by light of day?

WRITING PROMPT

Pretend the night has taught you all its lessons. In one magical, eight-hour period, everything you needed to know to craft a happy, brilliant, generous life has been revealed. Everything is obvious – you see your way, clear as day. Now what are you going to do with this precious life of yours? Use this section to write out your entire future. Share the revelations you received and shoot for the moon! What do you want, now that you know?

MIDNIGHT PAGES

MIDNIGHT PAGES

FERTILE TERRAIN

Think of night as a territory, a dark, rich, fertile, and mostly unexplored landscape you have the opportunity to travel through every twenty-four hours. It's a terra incognita because only the rare person takes the journey consciously. Most of us sleep right through it.

When the night is half over, you've just begun.

What if this week you decided to stay awake intentionally, even if it's just for an additional couple of hours, and imagined yourself on a trip through the night as if it were a foreign country? You could be a passenger on the Midnight Express or about to board the red-eye out of Los Angeles. Maybe you're climbing the gangway of a nineteenth-century ocean liner bound for another continent in another era. Time travel is allowed. Let each night be another leg of the journey. See where your imagination takes you.

For the writing exercise, I've given you a guided travelogue. Write about this unfamiliar land; journal your itinerary, the places you visit, the sights you see, and the people you meet. Let the shadows in your house become temples and castles. Let your imagination chatter in the voices of your travel companions. Listen for the "All aboard!" of the conductor, the staccato accent of your hosts. Let the crickets and cicadas, the wind, and the beating rain become the songs that reverberate through the bazaar or souq. Your imagination is heightened in the night, and it will guide you.

If you are a frequent traveler on the wings of the night, you might want to elevate the experience into a spiritual journey. If so, let it reveal truths. Let it change you. Remember the journey between Mecca and Jerusalem, which the Prophet Mohammed took before he ascended into heaven, is called The Night Journey. Maybe you will take your own pilgrimage between one holy city and another.

Search the darkness, don't run from it.
Night travelers are full of light,
and you are too... –Rumi

WRITING PROMPT: TRAVEL JOURNAL

Play along with me and see if you can think of your nights as times of wandering, adventure, and sight-seeing. Imagine, pretend, and create. This is a little travel journal—a book within a book—something you can use each night this week. It is meant for a trip of seven days, which seems just about long enough for now. So, stay up an extra couple of hours, imagining yourself on a brilliant, international (or interplanetary) trip. See the sights, meet the locals, bring back souvenirs. Bon voyage!

MY TRIP

TRAVELOGUE DAY ONE

LOCATION: Home.

Today my journey begins!

I'm leaving for _____, hoping to _____
_____

I'm excited to see _____ and taste _____ and
experience _____ firsthand.

I leave at ___ pm, when everyone else has fallen asleep. I am looking forward to _____
and I plan to watch for _____
and _____.

I feel _____ about this trip. I've been in this nighttime
country before, but I never _____.

This time I intend to _____
_____
_____
_____

I made sure to pack my _____.

Along the way, I plan to make stops at _____ and
I really want to observe _____ because _____.

They say travel opens the mind. This is what I want this trip to show me: _____.
As I set out, I am feeling _____.

MY TRIP

TRAVELOGUE DAY TWO

LOCATION: _____

I made it to _____! I notice that I _____
_____
_____
_____.

I feel _____.

I didn't expect to discover _____.

I've already met some interesting characters. They almost seem dreamlike!
There was _____ who was _____
_____and they _____
_____
_____.

and also _____who was _____
_____
_____.

I am starting to notice how different this world is than my life back home in the daylight.
For instance, _____
_____
_____
_____.

MY TRIP

TRAVELOGUE DAY THREE

LOCATION: _____

Thinking back over the past two days, I can't believe how far I've come. Everything looks different by night. I've _____

_____

And yet, _____

What has been unexpected on this trip is _____

I'm starting to wonder about what I used to call my "real" life. It's as if this unreal journey has become the *real* real. I lost a piece of luggage today. It contained my _____

_____ and I _____.

I'll have to do without it by _____.

Write a postcard to a friend or loved one back home. Tell them about your journey and what you are seeing along the way.

MY TRIP

TRAVELOGUE DAY FOUR

LOCATION: _____

What I am noticing tonight is _____
_____
_____

Sometimes I want to just go home and stop this crazy trip. I want to sleep and be normal like everyone else. But _____
_____

When I get home I am going to rearrange the _____ and get rid of my I have no interest or desire to go back to my routine and deal with _____

Maybe I will _____ when this trip is over.

Maybe I can _____.

I met a person on the train today who _____. They told me the strangest thing: _____
_____
_____

I actually shared some wisdom with them too. I said, _____
_____
_____

Since I will never see any of these people again, I realized I _____.

They taught me a game, _____, which, in hindsight, seems like a metaphor for life. It _____.

MY TRIP

TRAVELOGUE DAY FIVE

LOCATION: _____

I'm tired and I _____
_____
_____

But we had a big itinerary. It was the most arduous night so far. We climbed/trekked/swam
_____ to see
the sights of _____

I stood at the summit and thought _____
_____
_____

The whole experience left an impression on me because _____
_____
_____

I feel both exhilarated and also like it's a "dark night of the soul" because _____
_____
_____

Tonight, I feel homesick and very far from home. I _____
_____
_____
_____

MY TRIP

TRAVELOGUE DAY SIX

LOCATION: _____

I couldn't find an ATM today, and my cash is running low. I worry that _____ which reminds me of when I _____

I might have to rely on the generosity of my traveling companions or strangers, at least until we reach the mainland/city/civilization. I feel _____
_____
_____.

It was a bit of an adventure today when _____

And I felt nervous when _____

_____ can be a dangerous _____
_____
_____.

What always saves me in those moments is my _____

One more day and I really want to _____
_____
_____.

MY TRIP

TRAVELOGUE DAY SEVEN

LOCATION: _____

Today we head back to the mainland/city/civilization so we can be near the airport/seaport/ departure point.

I feel _____
_____
_____.

I want to soak up the local color, to remember what I discovered here in this country, _____
_____
_____.

I walked around the town by myself, looking for _____

I noticed _____.

And stopped to listen to _____ which made me

think about _____.

I will miss _____

I picked out some souvenirs for myself: _____

I chose these because _____

MY TRIP

TRAVELOGUE DAY SEVEN CONT.

In one final burst of creative imagination before I get on the train/plane/bus, I want to describe this one scene from the country where I visited: _____

_____

_____

_____

Forever etched in my memory is _____

_____

_____

And the time I _____

_____

From all the places I've been and the things I've seen, I will take _____

_____ with me. That was the night I _____

_____

_____

Bon Nuit!

MIDNIGHT PAGES

MIDNIGHT PAGES

IT WAS A DARK AND STORMY NIGHT...

Can you imagine how dark the nights were a hundred thousand years ago? Dark so complete on a moonless evening that you couldn't see your hand in front of your face. Night so deep that some nights, it'd make you dizzy, disoriented, unable to situate yourself in time or space. Is this where nyctophobia—fear of the night—comes from? I'm sure it's evolutionarily rooted. How could it not be? We lean toward the light like little sun flowers.

Let the day teach us what we must be and the night teach us what we are. –Unknown

Many religions use light as the ultimate metaphor for life, hope, and salvation. The Hebrew/Christian bible is rich with these images. Hymns and songs pit dark and light against each other in thousands of stanzas, little lyrics of good (light) and evil (dark).

The people who walked in darkness have seen a great light; those who dwelt in a land of deep darkness, on them has light shone.
–The Hebrew Bible, Isaiah 9:2

The light shines in the darkness, and the darkness has not overcome it. –The Gospel According to John, 1:5
(New International Version)

I wonder if the deep darkness drove some people to look within, to confront their mortality, or seek out the origin of their soul. Feeling puny and defenseless, did we search ourselves for the light of the divine to save us? When we were immersed in those darkest of nights; were we any closer to an enlightened state than we are today? Did the primitive, simple, terrifying dark make us more spiritual? Connect us more perfectly with our creator?

Seeing into darkness is clarity. –Lao-Tzu (translated by Stephen Mitchell)

All I know is when I sit to meditate during the day, I am distracted. All the pretty scenes outside my window grab my attention. The phone rings, I crave the rush of new email or a fresh post on some social media page. I remember that a show I wanted to watch is now available on Netflix. I am tempted to text someone or read a book or work. All these things compete with meditating or going within. Even our night is lit up with electricity, music, the sounds of traffic on the street. In an undisturbed deep darkness, would we be more spiritual? Would we feel more connected to the Infinite, to each other, to nature?

Well, this I know for sure, our ancestors were closer to the earth and more connected to the cycles of day and night, the seasons and moon phases. From that perspective they might have been less afraid of night than we are and more open to navigating by its signs. I like to believe that seeing the enormous sky full of stars each night would have been all they needed to discover their place in the fullness of space and time.

WRITING PROMPT

Just for tonight, don't use media. Don't read your texts. Don't turn on lights or television. Sit and be in the dark. Go outside if you can. What does it feel like? Connect with all the watchers of the night through all time. Write.

MIDNIGHT PAGES

MIDNIGHT PAGES

MIDNIGHT PAGES

NOCTURNALIS

Nocturnalis means "belonging to the night." If you are up and reading this, you qualify. Here you are in the middle of it, in this alternative state of awareness. What is different about the person you are now as opposed to who you are in the day?

The night is associated with magic, ghosts, and secrets, vampires, werewolves, dreams, and angel visitations. You are creating in the night, using it to gestate your ideas, plans, and books. You are letting things brew in the dark, not hurrying them to rise to the surface before they are ready.

Notes

Treasure the night because it is fragile. Up against artificial light and twenty-four-hour drive-through, is it only a matter of time before the night goes away completely? It is threatened with extinction by the endless news cycles and the internet which doesn't sleep and never needs so much as a nap.

New York was long ago called "the city that never sleeps," and that seemed like a badge of honor. It made me want to go there even more—this energetic, wakeful beast of insomniacs like me. But if you try to sleep in the city when you're not used to it, you know from the horns and sirens that what keeps the city from sleep isn't always welcome.

Protect the precious night. Don't turn on the lights if you wake up. Put up shades against the streetlights. Never flip on the TV or computer if you get bored. Let the dark be your incubator, a blank screen for you to create. Let it be the liminal, mystical space where ideas, desires, and visions are born that are just too big to fit into the thimble of the day.

WRITING PROMPT

Life is supposed to be an epic, creative adventure, a journey of imagination and wonder. How many people do you know who live like that? Probably not many. But you're one of the few, the chosen, a nighthawk. You already have a different perspective, and maybe you even hear the call to your epic adventure. I am calling you out, Heroine/Hero. What now?

MIDNIGHT PAGES

MIDNIGHT PAGES

MYSTICS AND DEVOTIONS

In the late Middle Ages, a popular style of book was written for people's private devotions. Called *A Book of Hours*, they were illustrated and detailed, no two exactly alike. They provided prayers or meditations for each hour of the day, the goal being to help the reader focus on the Divine at all times. In the midst of our daily lives, we were to stop and pray every hour. Having God in the back of our minds was not enough. Even the middle of the night was an important time to wake up and remember God's blessings.

Notes

In meditation let the person rouse himself from things temporal and let him collect himself within himself – that is to say, within the very center of his soul, where lies impressed the very image of God. –San Pedro de Alcantara

I doubt most people prayed on the hour all through the night. You'd be pretty useless during the day if you did. But there were mystics, monks, and contemplatives who devoted themselves in this way, and it was believed they were an integral part of society: this was the "work of the people," prayers done by the dedicated, which protected all the people of the faith.

WRITING PROMPT

This is a modified *Book of Hours*. It is designed to take you through the night with short meditations on the hour, beginning at midnight and going until six o'clock in the morning. Read, meditate, and write for at least thirty minutes each hour. If you get tired, remember during a vigil, you are watching for something; you are vigilant, looking for signs, portends, information that is key to your future. Approach it with that sort of urgency, and you probably won't feel like sleeping very much.

Research *Book of Hours* online and notice how they were illustrated and illuminated. If you're arty, you might want to create your own.

Write to me at *Diane@theMidnightpages.com* to tell me the results of your nightlong vigil. Send me your own book of hours, and maybe I'll post it up on the blog.

BOOK OF (MIDNIGHT) HOURS

12:00 AM

While all things were wrapped in peaceful silence
and night was in the midst of its swift course...
a secret world leaped down from heaven, to me...
–Meister Eckhart

Pick up your pen after ten minutes of meditation and let it move across the page. Begin by writing: What secret wants to leap down from heaven? What secret is arising from within? What secret is coming from Divine Inspiration? What secret comes from my muse? What secret is now coming to me? What do I need to know? What is the secret? What secret wisdom will I hear tonight? Repeat these questions as needed. See what else shows up. Write for thirty minutes. When you are done, read over what you've written. Do not share the secret with anyone.

BOOK OF (MIDNIGHT) HOURS

All shall be well and all shall be well,
And all manner of things shall be well. –Julian of Norwich

Vipassana Meditation is compassion meditation. You begin with yourself, saying some version of:

May I be well, may I be healthy and happy. May I be at peace.

Next, you offer the same blessing to people close to you.
Include people you may not be getting along with. Picture
them one at a time and for each person repeat:

May you be well. May you be healthy and happy. May you be
at peace.

Finally, send the blessing to the world saying:

May all beings be well. Maybe all beings be healthy and happy.
May all beings be at peace.

BOOK OF (MIDNIGHT) HOURS

As you think of all the people of the world, you might start with your neighborhood, then expand out to your city, state, nation, continent, then other continents and finally, the entire planet. Let your compassion expand and let yourself feel connected.

2:00 AM

...lying awake one sees more clearly in the dark, feels more intensely in the aloneness. –Elizabeth Yates

Make a list of everything you are afraid of. Don't stop until the list is fifty items long. Then list fifty reasons why there is no reason to fear them. Turn that list into a story that has a happy and courageous ending.

BOOK OF (MIDNIGHT) HOURS

3:00 AM

> *Let nothing disturb thee, Nothing affright thee.*
> *All things are passing. God never changeth.*
> —St. Teresa of Avila

Write the first sentences of five stories about how the peace is disturbed and calls a heroine to action out of her complacency, boredom, and fear. If you are so moved, pick one of the stories and finish it. No longer than three pages.

4:00 AM

> *(The one) who hurries, delays the things of God.*
> —Vincent de Paul

Practicing patience during this the vigil is key to finishing it. Write a story using the following words: Delays, orange, tube socks. If that doesn't feel cosmic or mystical enough, write a mystical story about delays, orange, and socks that go all the way up over your knee caps.

BOOK OF (MIDNIGHT) HOURS

5:00 AM

Patience gains all things. –Teresa of Avila

You're in the home stretch of this vigil now. The dawn may be breaking; you can feel the shift toward daylight. Write a list of fifty things you didn't know before tonight or fifty things you are grateful for, including all you've written and conjured up. If you're tired of all the listing, pick your pen up with your non-dominant hand and allow the child in you to write. Maybe it's his or her first sentence or the first time she got the assignment, "what I did on my summer vacation..."

BOOK OF (MIDNIGHT) HOURS

(God) giveth his beloved sleep.

–Psalm 127:2

The mystic poet Rumi writes, "The breezes at dawn have secrets to tell you." Go outside and watch the sun come up. What do the breezes of dawn tell you? Watch until the sun is fully in the sky then write an intention for the day before you end your vigil.

You can let the vigil mark the start of a new life. (Sounds dramatic, but so what?) What symbolic act might you finish off with? Is there something you can let go of or throw away? Decluttering is very freeing and shows you how you might be holding on to unnecessary things.

Another way to mark this new post-vigil day is ... (you choose.) Remember it's different today. Things will never be the same because you are different. This is a choice! Describe (on the next page).

REFLECTIONS ON THE BOOK OF HOURS AND THE NEW DAY

(lined writing space)

MIDNIGHT PAGES

MIDNIGHT PAGES

A SPELL OF VIGILANCE

Having spent more than a few pages on how mysterious and wonderful the early hours are and having told you all the lovely things you can do or observe during them, I have to acknowledge that the night isn't loved and appreciated by everyone. To the insomniac, it's a nemesis.

My father was an insomniac, so I have always assumed I inherited my sleep patterns from him. He compounded the issue by working a swing shift: eight to four, four to mid, (as he called it,) and midnight to eight. He'd get two days off in between and would sleep sporadically that whole time. His sleep—and his moods— got pretty screwy. Not good when you're bipolar to begin with.

As many as 30 percent of American adults experience insomnia on a short-term basis and 10 percent have long-lasting insomnia.[12] Some say the figures are even higher. If you suffer, you know. It shows up when you're struggling with other things: menopause or PTSD, for example. Sometimes it is recurrent and life-long and who knows why?

One the worst things about insomnia, aside from the exhaustion, the mood changes, the clumsiness, and the feeling of hopelessness, is the paradox that the harder you try to sleep, the worse the problem becomes. It's like *trying* to relax or to meditate. Sleep, relaxation, meditation just aren't states you can get to through effort.

"My doctor says I really better try to get more sleep," said one insomniac. As if a life-long pattern of staying up all night was going to turn around after a good scolding by the M.D. and a bit harder trying.

Worrying about the sleep we've "lost" and what it'll mean for the following day makes falling asleep even more elusive. What frustrated non-sleeper hasn't thought, "I have to get up in three hours. Tomorrow is going to be torture!"

> *"I feel so frustrated, I just cry..."*
> –a poster on more than one
> Facebook group

Notes

Can we make up for lost sleep? The answer flip-flops. I worried years ago when I heard about the dreaded "sleep deficit." Once you had one, you couldn't make up for it by sleeping in on the weekends or catching a nap in the afternoon. Then the news shifted, and I was elated! Yes, you can make up for lost sleep by napping on the weekends. I think the tides have turned once again (though I'm having a hard time keeping up). It seems that when it comes to a sleep deficit, if you're down a few, it's permanent. I'm deep in debt at this point.

We are born to be awake, not to sleep...
–Paracelsus, sixteenth-century
Swiss alchemist

WRITING PROMPT

Meet a Swiss banker and see if you can get him to unlock the vault to your sleep deficit. How will you convince him to let you count your zzzzs. What happens once you have *that*?

MIDNIGHT PAGES

MIDNIGHT PAGES

MIDNIGHT PAGES

PUTTING FEAR TO BED

Our sleeplessness isn't unnatural or even terribly unusual. Sleep psychologist Gregg Jacobs writes, "Waking up during the night is part of normal human physiology."[13] Phew, that's a relief. Russel Foster, who originated the idea of the body clock, called waking up in the middle of the night a "throwback to the bi-modal sleep pattern."[14] We talked about biphasic sleep earlier in the book. First and second sleeps are common knowledge as far back as the seventh century. For me, and I suspect for lots of people, biphasic sleep isn't a throwback at all. It's now.

Remember: You are awake for a reason: the night has something to tell you.

Notes

Teach me your mood, O patient star
Who climb each night in the ancient sky,
Leaving on space no shade, no scars,
No trace of age, no fear to die.
–Ralph Waldo Emerson

WRITING PROMPT

"Nothing from nothing comes" is a bit of alchemical wisdom. We assume the night is a "nothing," void, empty, meaningless. That's why we don't expect anything to come from it, except wasted hours when we should have been resting.

Prove that idea wrong by taking this night and generating alternatives, solutions, and insights to apply to your current situation. Let the energy of the night, which is anything but void and empty, inspire you. Plug into it like a power source. Write about imaginary solutions and improbable ideas that will change the world.

MIDNIGHT PAGES

MIDNIGHT PAGES

MIDNIGHT PAGES

VIGIL

Some nights, stay up till dawn,
As the moon sometimes does for the sun.

—Rumi

In my childhood church, we used to have an Easter vigil from Saturday night until Easter sunrise. I'd get pretty excited, but the sign-up sheet was usually hard to fill up.

I bet it was because the church had a reputation as haunted. One guy I knew, six-foot-four and two-hundred and sixty pounds of muscle, strong as a bull, refused to even enter the building at night. I never heard him speak about why. If you asked him, he'd get all cloudy and shake his head. He was a very sunny fellow, so it was jarring to see the change come over him. "C'mon, John! It's a church! What'd you see?"

Nothing. But one c is all it takes to change sacred into scared.

The fear we focus on grows.

It seems obvious that fear is what spurred us to develop things like faith, religion, and magic. Maybe that profound fear of dark and night and sleep and death is why we say prayers and wish upon stars.

Speaking of the moon and the stars, imagine what a blessing they must have been when they were the only things glowing up in the sky. No wonder the moon was (and is) associated with the benevolence of Goddess through so many cultures. Hers was the only face literally shining light on the human path. During the dark moon phase when She hid Her face, we can only imagine what sort of dangers lurked, especially from those under cover of the darkness who preyed upon the rest of us.

WRITING PROMPT

Sometimes, no words come. No matter how still the night or good the writing prompts. On those nights, take a shower. Daydream. Let your mind wander. Sing out loud. Intend nothing. Ask for nothing. Listen to the sounds of the house settling, the roommates snoring, the wind against the window. Know that your subconscious is on the job whether you're writing or not.

MIDNIGHT PAGES

*Rabi'a's Evening Prayer: O my Lord, the stars are shining
and the eyes of men are closed and kings have shut their
doors and every lover is alone with his beloved and here am
I alone with Thee.*[15]

MIDNIGHT PAGES

SOMNIO

Somnio means to drowse; it's that state of pleasant surrender before we fall asleep. I don't surrender well, so I resist. Less pleasant, more begrudging.

Sleep is its own weird thing, into which we "fall," and during which we experience phases that include paralysis, unconsciousness, and shutting down of the senses we need to stay vigilant. Science proves our brains stay active while we sleep, but anyone who has ever been jolted awake by a loud noise knows it's not the same type of brain activity as when we're awake and aware.

We surrender to sleep, but at least some part of us has always known we surrender to death in the same way. Is that the root of sleep dread or hypnophobia (the fear of falling asleep)?

Is that at the primordial root of the child's prayer?

Now I lay me down to sleep, I pray dear Lord my soul to keep. And if I die before I wake, I pray thee, Lord, my soul to take.

The poem dates to the eighteenth century, a time full of perils and dark nights.

How many poems and prayers from all over the world were written as wards against the gathering dark? Many. Take for example the evening prayers of the Eastern Orthodox church—the highest of "high church" traditions—where we find the acknowledge-ment of the surrender of sleep. The chant to protect us in that state goes:

All my hope I place in thee, O Theotokos,
(Mother of God).
Keep me under thy wing of care.

As I was writing this, I received an email saying, "You are most vulnerable when you arc asleep." Timely. But try as I might, I cannot figure out what's being advertised and what I am vulnerable to. It doesn't take much for me to fill in the blanks; there are plenty of fearsome things going on while I sleep. It's one of the reasons I don't prefer it. The advertiser knows that, at least for some of us, somnophobia is encoded into our cells.

WRITING PROMPT

This prompt is best if you're
suffering a bout of insomnia...

What would you call this sleeplessness spell
you are under? *Think back to when it began.*
What else was going on at the time? What
associations do you have to those events? Were
they resolved?

If this were a fairy tale, who cast the spell
of sleeplessness and what keeps you in
its thrall? *Who does your antagonist remind*
you of? How and why are you bound to
him or her?

What will break the spell? *What must you do or believe? What magic words do you have to say to right your life, to put your insomnia to bed for good? As you know, words have power. Write the formula or the incantation for your healing.*

MIDNIGHT PAGES

MIDNIGHT PAGES

MIDNIGHT PAGES

LAST NIGHT

If you are a writer, of course you will have some writerly resistance; that's not only a daytime occupation. Even in the middle of the night, we can find ways to resist. We procrastinate: we'll make tea, find our favorite blanket, pile it on the couch with the perfect notebooks, pens, and the laptop. We will sit and sip and check TikTok, scroll the messages. Then if we haven't gotten too sleepy, we'll write. That is unless we get overwhelmed. We'll write unless we look back on what we've written so far and then, we judge ourselves; this nighttime writing is gibberish! But, none of these forms of resistance is any match for the powerful magic of the night.

Notes

I urge you, then, pursue your course relentlessly. Attend to tomorrow and let yesterday be. Never mind what you have gained so far. Instead reach out to what lies ahead. –The Cloud of Unknowing, William Johnston, Ed.

Let night be your collaborator. Allow the magic of piling up words until there is something. Page upon page, insight upon insight, scene upon limping, imperfect scene. What are you coming to know about yourself, your characters, the story? Right now, in the middle of the night, you have a new perspective on it all: you are set apart, awake, and writing when the world is not.

If you are a writer, remember, the power of the night is to make your horror story creepier, your thriller or mystery more mysterious, your romance even steamier. You can turn your meet-cute into a scene as touching as only a scene under the moonlight can be. If you stay up until dawn, go watch it. As the sun comes up imagine how your story has come out of the dark—you've gone down into the night and into the unconscious mind and come out with a new creation, even if it is only a sentence, an idea, a solid scene, a book.

If you are using automatic or inspired writing in order to journal more deeply or to figure out your insomnia or to sort out your life, I assure you the night has something to tell you. You are awake for a reason. Don't let this holy, wakeful moment escape.

> *Give up one night to the vigil.*
> *Don't sleep.* –Rumi

If you saw the night as your collaborator, what would you do together?
Personify the night. What would you
have with her by your side?

MIDNIGHT PAGES

MIDNIGHT PAGES

FINAL WRITING PROMPT (FOR NOW)

If you could dial in inspiration, (or brilliant ideas for your book, or the perfect solution to the dilemma you're facing right now), like tuning your old radio to a station on the AM dial, what's playing? Country western, NPR? Top 40? What's the station's jingle? What song is on the air right now? Why is it perfect for you?

MIDNIGHT PAGES

AND TO ALL A GOOD NIGHT!

I hope you've enjoyed your first taste of Midnight Pages and that they will become a lifelong habit. Please let me know how you write them: faithfully every night at midnight, or sporadically when you find yourself unable to sleep. Tell me about your shifts and insights; about the ways the night has shared inspiration and direction and what you now think about staying up past your bedtime.

If you are interested in wild explorations of the night and more writing prompts, come visit me at www.themidnightpages.com and sign up for membership in the Midnight Writing Circle. It's a community where you can write within the high vibe energy of other like-minded folk. You can enter contests and win prizes, get feed-

Notes

back on your writing and more. On the blog you will find more creative writing inspiration and thoughts about the night, guidance for Midnight Pages and information about High Vibe Soul Deep Writing™ retreats and classes as well as the much anticipated Magical Writing Guild for Girls.

ENDNOTES

1 High Vibe Soul Deep Writing is a group experience for writers of all levels. We use fun, creative exercises and writing prompts to spark the imagination and get unstuck. It's also great for writers who want to jazz up their prose. If you are curious or want even more prompts, visit *www.thewritewitch.com* and you will find writing inspiration, downloadable PDFs with exercises and advice about how to connect with your Muse, and useful tips about all things author.

2 Snyder F., *Toward an Evolutionary Theory of Dreaming* (Am. J. Psychiatry, 1966), 123, 121–136, https://doi:10.1176/ajp.123.2.121

3 David R. Samson, Alyssa N. Crittenden, Ibrahim A. Mabulla, Audax Z. P. Mabulla and Charles L. Nunn, *Chronotype variation drives night-time sentinel-like behaviour in hunter-gatherers* (Published:12 July 2017), https://doi.org/10.1098/rspb.2017.0967

4 A. Roger Ekirch, *At Day's Close: Night in Times Past*, W.W. Norton: NY, 2005

5 A. Roger Ekirch, *At Day's Close: Night in Times Past* (WW Norton and Co., New York and London, 2005) pg. 303.

6 Robby Berman, in an article in *Big Think* (10 April 2018) writes that researchers believe the practice of sleeping through the night didn't really take hold until a few hundred years ago.

7 Ezenwanne E., "Current Concepts in the Neurophysiologic Basis of Sleep; a Review" (*Ann Med Health Sci Res.* 2011;1(2)), 173-179, https://www.ncbi.nlm.nih.gov/pmc/articles/PMC3507109/

ENDNOTES CONT.

8 Browse U Magazine, "Our Ancestors Probably Didn't Get Eight Hours of Sleep a Night, Either," https://www.uclahealth.org/u-magazine/our-ancestors-probably-didn-t-get-eight-hours-of-sleep-a-night-either

9 *www.thewritewitch.com*, *www.bellywitch.com*, *www.themidnightpages.com*, *www.earthandsoulpublishing.com* will take you to classes, retreat dates, and more writing tips, prompts, and suggestions than you can probably ever use. You can also join one of my Facebook groups: Midnight Pages and The Belly Witch.

10 Ekirch, pg.207

11 Craig Koslovsky, *In Evening's Empire: A History of Night in Early Modern Europe*, (Cambridge University Press, 2011) pp. 75-76.

12 The Recovery Village, "Insomnia Facts and Statistics," April 14, 2021, https://www.therecoveryvillage.com/mental-health/insomnia/insomnia-statistics

13 Stephanie Hegarty, "The myth of the eight-hour sleep," *BBC News*, February 22, 2012, https://www.bbc.com/news/magazine-16964783

14 Robby Berman, "For thousands of years, humans slept in two shifts. Should we do it again?" *Big Think*, April 10, 2018, https://bigthink.com/robby-berman/for-1000s-of-years-we-went-to-bed-twice-a-night-2

15 Thomas Craughwell, Editor, *Every Eye Beholds You: A World Treasury of Prayer* (Book of the Month Club, 1998), p. 40. Rabïa al-Adawiyya (717-801) was a Sufi saint and mystic who lived in Basra. She took a vow of chastity and devoted herself to God. A biographer of Safi'a's has said that after dark she would go up on the roof of her home and begin her evening devotions with this prayer.

Printed in Great Britain
by Amazon